THE LONG NIGHT'S WALK

Alan White

POPULAR LIBRARY • NEW YORK

CHAPTER ONE

They had possession of the wood, and therefore Simon knew he dare not use the bridge. The next bridge downriver was at least four miles and who knows, perhaps they also had possession of that or had mined it to blow skyhigh at the first foot-fall. He carried on, slowly, down the lane at right angles to the bridge. He was safe on this side of the water only for as long as he could keep within shelter of the buildings. He turned and looked back. Sammy was where he should be, on the roof just beneath the funny-shaped bell-tower that had no bell. "Smelted down for bullet cases," he thought, but he must stop that, drifting into irrelevancies. Stay with the matter on hand. They had to cross a river and quickly or the straps of this hundred-pound pack would cut his shoulder flesh to ribbons. And time was getting on.

Slowly he raised the barrel of the rifle, his eyes restless, looking everywhere. Bloody old Lee-Enfield, what a weapon with which to send a man to war. Why not a Schmeizer, semi-automatic? Or even a shotgun, come to think of it. There was a suspicion of movement along the line of the corner by that building, an old stables it must once have been. He brought the rifle to the firing position at his waist. That gesture would alert the rest of them. He beckoned Jonfey to come forward. Jonfey came down the side of the building, a dull khaki blur against the brown of the stonework. Jonfey would be able to see round that corner. There was a suspicion of movement in the upstairs window of the building on the left; that would have been a farm worker's cottage, wouldn't it, in peacetime long long ago. Up this lane farm carts would bring the harvest; "twenty acres today," the farmer would boast and they'd break out the drink and cheese, thick hunks of harvest bread and butter . . . Steady on, keep your mind on that upstairs window that contains the merest whisper of movement. Watch it, Jonfey; as usual you're going too far too fast. Hold it there in the doorway while someone else leapfrogs past you. I can't cover you past that building on your left, you bloody fool; you ought to know it's outside my line of fire.

5

Jonfey stopped in the doorway. "Mustn't go any further," his mind commanded, "or you'll be out of Simon's line of fire, and if someone jumps you from a doorway, God help you." A piece of rag was caught in the crook of a post against the building on the other side of the alley. "Bet that gave Simon a scare," he thought, "from back there it must look like someone moving."

He pointed his finger at the object, his thumb stuck downwards in a signal they all knew as 'no target'. That'd reassure Simon. Jonfey turned and looked back. Simon and Sammy smiled, Fred smiled, they all smiled. A regular bunch of laughing cavaliers, weren't they? But this was no joke, was it, this was 'for real' as they say. Simon pointed at the window high in the building opposite. There was a sudden flick of movement. Jonfey held his thumb and forefinger to his nose; 'it stinks', the gesture said, only one of fifty gestures they had learned in training. This one implied, 'I do not like what I can see.' Simon held up his finger, then described a rapid ascending spiral; 'go around and investigate', that one meant. There was a low wall; bent double Jonfey raced along it across a six-foot opening, moving fast, lost to view. No covering fire, no rifles in friendly hands waiting to bark at anyone attacking him. This one you did on your own. Round the back of the building hugging close to the stones. A window. Bend down. A door, straight past it; it's closed, thank God. God's working overtime today. The next window doesn't exist any more. The glass, the frame, and half the brickwork has been blown away. Quick decision? Yes, jump in everything at the ready, over the crumbling brickwork land in a crouch. Hand down the side of your right leg near the knife, other hand back along the rifle to the trigger guard ready to pump one. Oh, these bloody Lee-Enfield rifles, sticking out in front of you like a permanently hard but useless prick. Why don't they issue pistols, cold-nosed colt four-fives that stop an elephant.

Stand perfectly still, Jonfey, no, for Christ's sake don't overbalance forwards. The floor's mined and you're standing on the wire. The mine was right under the window and you missed it by a sparrow's fart, but, you're standing on the wire Jonfey. Is it a release mechanism? Have you tripped the first part? There's no fuse, you'd have heard it crack or smelled it. If you've armed it by treading on the wire, when you move your foot off the wire, there'll be a bang and your balls will splatter the ceiling like spaghetti bollocknese. Quick look round. No-one in the room; door to the hallway open, no-one there. Bend down. Feel for the mechanism. Careful,

careful! A wire had been stretched the entire width of the window about a foot from the wall, an inch and a half high. The centre of the wire was attached to a round tin, the size of four ounces of tobacco. In the centre of the tin was a round brass piece, like the top of a homemade cigarette lighter. He kept his foot on the wire and bent even further down. "Ah, you old Sod!" he said, jubilant. "I know you, you old Sod." He lifted his foot clear. Thank God for the mine recognition lessons held a hundred years ago it seemed, in the front room of a former boarding house in Scarborough. This was an old favourite. It was safe, as long as you didn't actually step on it or pull that wire. Jonfey chuckled, then wiped the cold fear sweat running down his forehead. He crossed the room, through the hallway and ran lightly up the stairs keeping to the ends of the tread. Upstairs was no sign of human life, no small noises or smells, the air heavy only with the dry odour of dust and decay. He took his knife from the cloth sheath in his trouser seam, placed his rifle on the floor by the door, grasped the knob and with one single movement flung open the door, jumped through the aperture and against the wall, his left hand pressed hard back ready to spring him in any direction. There was no-one in the room. A curtain, formerly red now bleached muddy brown, was tattered like a first war flag, flapping idly at the window. One tatter hung at arm height, another could have been a leg. The curtain looked as if it had been standing there since nineteen-eighteen. It could still have been mistaken for a human figure moving there in the half light of the gloom beside the window. "What a bloody war this is when we risk a mine for a curtain." But, it could have been a man, the man could have held a gun, and the gun could have coughed death. He took his green beret and poked it out of the window on the end of his rifle. No-one shot at it. He stood in the window and briefly gave the 'no target' symbol. To it he added one not in the book; two fingers spread wide apart lifted rapidly twice in a jerking movement. That was for the grenade, the fear, the pants-messing stomach-heaving bladder-opening fear that only recently had he learned to control.

They advanced, leapfrogging each other until they came to the banks of the river eight hundred yards from the edge of the wood. The sentry on the bank was child's play. He'd been smoking, was hiding in a hole, and didn't see or hear a thing until they dropped on him like a load of horseshit. Crossing the river was easy. They swam, fully clothed carrying packs and rifles clear of the water. Simon and Jonfey held Simon's hundred-pound pack between them. On the far bank they ran together up into the hedgerow then lay down shivering. "I didn't realise how warm it was in Loch Lochie in January," Jonfey said through chattering teeth.

"Everything's going too easily," Simon said, "I don't like it. I get the feeling we're being led forward into something."

They advanced into the field and lay down at right angles to each other, covering the arc of fire while the other six men came across the river and up into the hedge. As soon as the men were ready Fred gave Simon the 'all right to advance' signal, and they moved forwards crawling steadily through the thick wet grass. The cutting was only two hundred and fifty yards ahead of them. Two on the far side, two on the near bank, two watching north and east, two south and west. The Army says you must do everything in pairs. Jonfey and Fred crossed the branch line and climbed the far bank. Simon and Matthew worked on the near bank, digging and planting. When they had finished they tamped the earth down on to the guncotton charges, ran the coil of wire along the top of the embankment for two hundred yards along the direction in which the train would come. Matthew placed a detonator on the line, acid/perchlorate type. When the weight of the train came to crush the detonator, the banks would fall on and in front of the train; it was Simon's own variation of the line smashing technique. Simon, in charge, checked his watch. The train was due in five minutes. He inspected the entire operation then ordered withdrawal.

I don't know why Sammy did it; perhaps exhilaration, perhaps relief. Suddenly he got to his feet, ran, and tried to longjump one of the water culverts. It was a good fourteen feet; he would have needed Olympic abilities. His jump was over two feet short; there was an agonised shout as he scrambled in the brickwork for a hold and then his fingers caught the gap between two bricks, a mere half inch, and held. His feet scrabbled along the culvert, and the rubber cleated soles of his commando boots found a tiny crevice. He hung there for several seconds, but then his fingers lost their grip, his body arced back from the brickwork and he fell to the bottom of the culvert, back cracking flat, sprawled inert among the broken slabs. "Quick," Simon said. "Down there and get him out—you Jonfey, you Matthew . . ."

At that moment I copped the back of his neck with the hard heel of my hand and Simon fell to the ground. I raised the Verey pistol and fired a starshell; it burst white above us. Then, all hell was let loose. Percussion grenades fell amongst us like hailstones—over to the left a machine gun opened fire on fixed lines, its tracer content spewing blood red and blue at a body height of three feet. We had all dropped to the ground, myself included. I was the training officer and they weren't shooting at me, but a white armband doesn't give immunity and though the cutting led only to an old mine shaft in the Brecon Beacons and the men behind the guns were the next section waiting their training turn, on my own instructions they were firing real live bullets.

"Private Arnold," I shouted, "you take over and get your section to hell out of here." He was a Methodist and wouldn't like me swearing, but what the hell. I fired the Verey pistol again and on sight of the red star the Bren gun stopped. Now the two-inch mortars lobbed smoke bombs and an acrid yellow-white fog began to conceal the countryside, to make it harder for the section to find their way home.

One of the men of the section, when he saw the smoke bombs begin to fall, came across the field to me, stood in front of me, and saluted. I saluted him back; I knew what he was going to say. The formality made it easier.

"You said that any time we didn't feel up to it, Captain, we should come to see you."

"Yes, John?" We'd dispensed with surnames many months before. "I can't take any more," he said, "seeing Sammy back there, and you giving the chop to Simon, and the thought of swimming that ice-cold river again, with the Bren gun shooting away at us. I can't take any more." There was no trace of hysteria. It was simply true—he couldn't take any more. That was what it was all about, wasn't it, in a sense. I was testing these men to the limits of their endurance, deliberately trying to break as many of them as I could. It was brutal, but time was not on our side. We were seventy-two men in a camp in North Wales learning to jump by parachute, to swim in icy water wearing boots, to throw a knife, shoot a bow and arrow, stab someone to death with our brand of knitting needles, hide our bulk behind two blades of bent grass, but above all to survive. I hoped that after what I was doing to these seventy-two volunteers, anything the Germans might do would be child's play.

"You know the drill, John. Get into the ambulance and get warm, and as soon as we can we'll take you back to camp." I never argued, never condemned. For obvious reasons we always kept an ambulance within easy distance; it was an added temptation to the lads to know it was kept warm inside, and there was always hot tea and food laid on.

We started out with a hundred men, but as they used to say, I could be a right bastard.

Simon stirred and recovered consciousness. He sat up and looked ruefully at me. "So that's what they all call 'the Captain's chop', is it?" "I hope it didn't disappoint you? You know why you got it, of course?" "Yes, sir. Trying to rescue Sammy. He was injured through his own silly fault; we should have left him. How is he, by the way?" "I don't know," I said, "I haven't looked. But that's not important, Simon." I tried to soften the tone of my voice—this wasn't a man to browbeat; his intellignece was as large as my own, in every way but one he was my equal. The exception, I was a Captain, he by choice a private. I was the trainer, he the one being trained. Sammy could be dead—I dare not care!

"The safety of any one man must be secondary," I said, repeating a well-worn lesson. "It doesn't matter whose fault it was, you had to leave him lying there. You couldn't get down there without endangering the success of your mission —dammit the train was due in only a few minutes—and, though once again I stress this is a secondary consideration, if you had gone down there you would have endangered the lives of other men and the effectiveness therefore of your striking force."

"We cannot help being what we are, sir, human beings."

"You must. You're a volunteer commando, just as I am. The day you volunteered you stopped being a human being. The minute you drew that knife from the quartermaster's stores, you accepted that if the need arose, you'd stick it into someone. That is not the way of a human being."

He was slowly recovering from the effects of the chop, rubbing the back of his neck. This was the last training we would all do together. Very soon I would need to make a final selection of these men, and those who survived I would take into Europe with me. And that would be the 'real thing', as Jonfey would have called it. The particular brain children of an otherwise sterile Major in the War Office, we were destined to be fleas that irritate, gremlins, poltergeists, kinks in the wire. We were going into the enemy lines, to make life as difficult for the troops there as it was possible to be. We were a legalised force of piss-takers, a Special Group.

But unlike all the other Special Groups, we would be dropped and left to our own devices. It was going to be that kind of war, for us. "Ivan Petrovitch Pavlov . . ." I said, but he interrupted me. "Nobel Prize Winner of 1904. 'All acquired habits depend on a chain of conditional reflexes'. He proved it with dogs. Pavlov's dogs. I know what you're trying to do to us. You're taking over where the drill sergeant leaves off. When he shouts 'hup' we click our heels together;

when you shout 'hup', without stopping to ask human questions, or have human doubts, we stick a knife into somebody."

"Or they stick it into you."

"Kill or be killed—it's a damned good slogan."

"Conditioned reflex. That means that, when you see a man, one man out of eight, fall into a ravine, your chain of conditioned reflexes passes the order to get to hell out of it, without a second thought. Can't you get that, Simon?"

"I can get it. I believe in Pavlov." He climbed to his feet; unconsciously dusting his hands against his uniform. "I can get it, but by God, there's nothing says I have to like it!"

"Think of Pavlov's dogs, they rang a bell for food and all they got was saliva."

"Yes, I'll think of Pavlov's dogs," he said as he started to jog trot after his section.

I let him get about ten paces then levelled my pistol, aiming at his back; I lifted the muzzle slightly. I hated to do it, but I squeezed the trigger. One, two, three. He was flat on the ground before I could squeeze off the second shot; during the second shot he rolled over and over; before I could fire the third time, his knife came winging through the air towards me.

Had I not been prepared the knife would have stuck in my throat; as it was, it sliced into the epaulette of my battledress jacket and I felt blood start to run down my shoulder.

"Well done," I said.

He looked up at me, a laugh amidst the tears already in his eyes. "Woof woof!" he said, got to his feet, plucked the knife out of my shoulder, turned, and ran away into the manmade fog.

CHAPTER TWO

I knew something was wrong the moment I stepped to the door of the plane. I was to be first out, the red light was on, and the ring at the end of my parachute line was hooked onto the rail. We were to drop in Holland, the other side of the Maas. It was one of those crystal-clear nights—the river shone below us, coiled, expectant. No clouds in the sky, and no rain. Dammit—the briefing officer promised us rain and thick cloud. "There won't be a living soul with his eyes turned skywards," he had promised at the tiny airport along the Pilgrim's Way near Canterbury.

The green light came on next to the red, and the despatcher tapped my shoulder; I stepped out, the sergeant, Simon and Jonfey behind me. Slip stream from the plane carried us backwards, loose, free falling, then the sudden balls-jarring snap as we reached the end of the line. Fixed line jumping was still experimental in those days—that's why we needed four starters for a three-man job. The bag snapped open, the pilot chute jerked clear, and the canopy of the big chute unfurled itself. Once again you felt as if you owned your stomach. Now we were on our way down through a sky powdered with starlight and a flaming moon, with at least a thousand Mausers and Schmeizers and a regiment of anti-aircraft guns slumbering on the ground below us. Talk about 'Ill met by bloody moonlight!' That slumber could end with the call of one moonstruck sentry, gazing at the star-spangled sky, dreaming of the fat sensuous arms of his liebling on the other side of the banks of the Rhine—one yelp as our canopies reflected the moonlight and a million vicious throats would cough venomous death at us. Damn the briefing officer—he promised us rain and a cloudy sky! The sergeant was swinging about fifty feet beside me, Simon and Jonfey over to his left. We still had a thousand feet to go. He looked up at the stars and I saw him frown and shake his head, that's how bright the moon was. "Let's get the hell out of here," his look implied. I reached up and grabbed the ropes fastened to the front end of the canopy. He saw the movement, and he too reached up. The message flashed as a cosmos to the other two, and we all pulled hard, spilling air from the back of the canopy, driving the chutes forwards and downwards through a stomach-yanking hundred-and-fifty-feet slip. Slowly I stopped pulling off centre, eased my hands down the ropes and let the canopy fill evenly again. Now we were off course. I reached up far behind me and pulled the back cords, air spilled from the front of the canopy, and we yawed backwards and downwards. "People pay good money and queue for this at Blackpool," I thought as Simon and Jonfey yawed down level with me. Jonfey, however, impetuous as ever, mistimed his recovery, and went swinging past me, missing the sergeant's chute by a matter of feet. I looked down in time to see him recover forty feet vertically below. "It would serve the young devil right if I were to land right on top of him," but a gust of wind pulled him to the side. When his chute moved over, I could see the ground below, identify the topography we had studied on a flour-and-water model knocked up for us in the back room of a house in Braintree, Essex. The river was where they had said it would be, and there the concrete works. There the two woods, side by side but separated by a thin strip of copse. The farm-house, with its outbuildings, and the other farmhouse—occupied by the Signals Headquarters. Below presumably were all the things the briefing officer had told us about but we couldn't see—the anti-aircraft battery in the wood to the left, the battalion of infantry in the wood to the right, mines in the fields around the woods. All that in a brief glance, and then there was no more time. We were coming in to land, and my under-carriage was shaking with fear.

There's nothing difficult about parachute jumping. It's the landing that bothers you. You come to earth with the impact of a jump off a twenty-foot wall. That's unloaded! Carry fifty pounds of equipment and the twenty becomes twenty-five and the risks of a broken leg or ankle that much greater. Now here was the ground. I can still see it clearly. I was going down forwards at an angle of about fifteen degrees, clipping twelve feet above the hedge. Let's hope the field beyond was clean of mines. The briefing officer didn't *think* this one was mined—but he didn't think there'd be stars and a moon. Jonfey down before me and rolling forward. Pulling the cords out of his chute. No mines, apparently. Sergeant next, no time to look at him. Ground now thirty feet below twenty now ten and the spine-jarring impact feels as if your parachute never opened. Now you roll forwards, bend the knees going slightly to the side since you've got this blasted pack on and if you roll straight you'll snap your spine, half roll sidewards and damn, into the rigging lines so twist sidewards and half roll again, down backwards and lie flat for a second, no more, turn over on your face, hands reaching down to your waist to unclip the seating harness that chafed your balls raw. You'd think they'd invent a better seat to pass through your legs than this tight canvas that gets you every way. Some men get an erection the minute the light comes on for jumping—that canvas nappie'd be enough to take the end off it! I lay on my side. A German in the hedge, ten feet away, was watching me. We must have woken him up. Doing sentry duty fast asleep in the hedge when we four come tumbling right over his head. The German was looking straight at the sergeant's back. Jonfey and Simon were facing the other way. The German had his hand on the Schmeizer trigger; pull that, you bastard, and the sergeant gets a burst of ten straight up his jaxi.

The German didn't know how many of us were coming down—four he could probably manage, but not a whole platoon. I was the last and any moment he'd waken to the fact we were only four, and spray us like greenfly on a dry summer's evening. I aimed my knife for his hands, but it stuck in his throat, and when I jumped over there seconds after the knife, the bubbles had started to come through the froth of blood. I pulled out the knife and that's what really killed him—the air rushed out from the dark hole where the blade had been—his head gave a couple of short convulsions, he twitched, and was dead.

The others had heard and seen the slight movement of my dash forward, and disappeared into the grass. I half stood up, under the hedge, searching the perimeter of the field with rapid backwards and forwards movements of my head. No other sentries. I could smell the acrid smoke on the German's head—he must have nipped through the hedge for a quick smoke. That put the rest of the sentries, for there were bound to be more, on the other side of this hedge, and it put us between them and their camp. I lifted my hand and made a sign above my head. Within seconds Jonfey, Simon and the sergeant were by my side, though I couldn't see them until they were only eight feet away.

"Everyone all right?" I whispered.

"Marvellous," Jonfey said. "I was dragged through a cow pat!" I could see the brown streak down the side of his face, and the side of his hair was covered in it. He scrubbed it out as best he could with a bunch of long grass, and then I gave him my water bottle to finish it off. The sergeant was looking speculatively over the field.

"Glad to be back?" I asked him.

He turned his head round in the direction from which we had come. "It's a long way home," he said. "Let's hope we don't have to walk it, and swim!"

"You all right, Simon?"

"I banged my elbow when I came down, but nothing serious. It will be all right soon." There was no point to me looking at it—Simon was a vet before the war, and should know about bones.

This was the first time I had set foot on the soil of the continent of Europe since Dunkirk—and that seemed a whole war away. I don't know what I'd been expecting—it's hard to imagine, for instance, that though a country is completely overrun and occupied, there can be physical gaps in the defences through which four men can drop unobserved by parachute. A canopy is such a damned great thing, floating down through the sky—visible, I would have thought, from twenty miles. Possibly, hopefully, the one man who'd see it was fifteen miles away; I had a ludicrous vision of him riding towards us, hell for leather, on a bicycle. All about us was a silence so complete I could hear each of us breathing from the exertion of the descent and the rapid change of air pressures. It was a dry night and clear, the air light crystal that carries sounds and scents; a marvellous night to be on the moors with a rabbit gun, a flask of brandied coffee, a roast beef sandwich and a lifetime of no wars stretching before you.

Seventy-two men and I had chosen two and the sergeant. It was too late now to wonder if I had made the right choice, but many nights since I had been told of this mission had been sleepless. Most of the seventy-two men had eliminated themselves in one way or another—some had been incompetent, incapable of learning the complex techniques of stalking, of moving at night without sight or sound. Those who could do this satisfactorily had no ability for the mechanical side of things, arming grenades, preparing explosive charges, defusing mines. We'd lost eleven men alone in the mines training. I didn't feel responsible for their deaths, though I had marched them into the lonely brick cubicles in the middle of the moor where, with the best training we could give them on dummies, eventually they had to be left alone with the real thing. Eleven had muffed it, from fear or incompetence we'd never know. Many men could handle the mechanics and the stalking, but oddly enough failed in such simple things as map reading, and routine signals procedure.

One man could do everything required of him on the moors, but just couldn't tune a radio to a correct frequency.

On the day of the final choice, I had the seven survivors in to see me, one by one. They had been through the hands of the medical officers, and all were physically fit. The psychiatrist, however, eliminated three of them. It was the last straw. Throughout their training they received regular checks from the psychologists; the excitement, however, of being on the border line of selection had tipped them over the edge.

Simon or Sammy, Jonfey or Matthew. This was another Sammy, not the one who'd thrown himself into the culvert, this was Sammy the tailor, a young Jewish boy brought up in the East End of London. Sammy had worked for a record-making company, and knew all there was to know about electronics. At the start of the war, when electronics were drafted into the military, Sammy became a tailor, and a pacifist. He stuck it for a year, then joined the Royal Corps of Signals and volunteered, as soon as it became possible, for Special Services. Matthew and Sammy made a good team, Jonfey and Simon made a good team, which should I choose. Then, almost immediately after my interview with him, Matthew went out and killed himself. He left a note addressed to me. All the time we had been training, he had hoped to be eliminated on some technical ground. He couldn't bring himself to quit. He never dreamed he could get through to the final selection, or that I'd ever say to him that I was putting him on the shortlist. When I knew Matthew had died I went to the half colonel who commanded our comic outfit, and asked him to remove the psychiatrists and psychologists—I had made the mistake of thinking theirs was an exact science.

My final choice was a simple matter of personality. Simon and Jonfey were a team, Sammy was a lone wolf. I felt he would always be a lone wolf, and that wouldn't do if four of us were to fight, hand in hand. I told Sammy myself I wasn't taking him. "Oh well," he said, "I suppose this is a job for the goyim." He didn't translate.

Simon had been a vet when he joined our unit, a vet with a public-school history and a love of animals both of which had bred in him a profound disrespect for the vagaries of the human species. You'd never catch Simon napping. Tall and slender, he looked as if a good wind would snap his spine. Yet he could walk into a field full of raging bulls, pick the fiercest, and lift its front hoof off the ground as if inviting it to dance. I once saw him hoist a full-grown ram onto his back, and carry it down ten miles of Welsh mountainside to treat legs broken by a fall from the top of a rock. All the way down the ungrateful beast kept pissing on his shoulder and the boys in the barrack room made Simon give his denims to the quartermaster before they'd let him in. Jonfey had been a horse breeder—ran a small stud in Northamptonshire of first-class hunters and show ponies for the county well-to-do. There wasn't a bone in his body hadn't been broken at some time or another. When Jonfey was mounted, you couldn't tell where he ended and the horse began. He had a grip with his knees that could bruise a bar of iron—his favourite party trick was to hang upside down from a wooden beam by his knee grip alone. They say the girls were most impressed by Jonfey, but that's something I took care not to know about.

We trained the seventy-two men for months in the Welsh mountains above Rhayader, stalking sheep and each other. The sergeant and I would sit on a knoll, each with a rifle loaded with live tracer bullets. Whenever we saw an arse sticking up out of the heather we'd put a shot as close to it as possible. I was brought up on the Yorkshire moors above Settle, and played with a shotgun before I had my first rattle. I could split a willow wand at a hundred paces, and some of my boys had an uncomfortable time. It taught them, however, to move inconspicuously over open country, to press their bellies into whatever depression they could find, to slide into stream beds and heather clumps, to crawl, and run bent double, and above all to arrive unseen at whatever destination we cared to choose. Seventy-two bloody fools since they chose to fight the war away from the comfortable trammels of Army discipline. They all called me 'sir' but I liked to deceive myself that was from respect, not fear. The sergeant they called 'Sarge', and without a doubt that was from respect. He was a six-foot-two monster of a man, with physical strength and agility in an unusual combination. Before the war he'd run around a foundry in the Ruhr with a tub of molten metal that weighed three hundred-weight, and never spilled a drop.

Our instructions were very simple, and the operation had been planned with the precision of a Cook's tour. From Canterbury we'd fly to Holland, where we'd disembark (by parachute). We'd remain in Holland for thirty-six hours and then fly back to Canterbury. It was as simple as that, and no tickets or passports were required. But while in Holland, we had to upset the working of an entire Signal Headquarters without being seen or doing any damage that would cause the Germans to suspect our presence. An entire Army was lodged in the valley over the hill, and that Army depended on this Signal Headquarters. There was to be an 'action in force' on the other side of that Army, and though the War Office had not yet learned to confide in Captains, I could guess it was something important. Our mission was to ensure the Signals Headquarters failed to operate efficiently at the vital time—how we were to do that was left to us. It was a mission after my own heart—a nice messy job of buggering someone about, and a lot of freedom in the manner of doing it. I had, however, been told that thousands of lives depended on us doing the job well, and that took the edge off the fun. In thirty-six hours we were to withdraw, to be picked up by a fast airplane flown, I had been promised, by a pre-war ace from Cobham's Flying Circus who could land and take off again on a handkerchief. He'd need his abilities when the time came—if they spotted us we'd be flying along a six-mile corridor of flaming ack-ack fire.

Jonfey and Simon had made a pact out there on the Welsh hillside above Rhayader, and in the simulated battlefields around the Brecon Beacons—what one didn't know the other would teach him. It had earned them a place on this first assignment. What a world of difference was in the two men. Simon was determined to be on it because to him it was unthinkable that another should do it in his place. As simple as that. There was a job we had to do, and either he came along, or someone came instead of him, and that was unthinkable. Jonfey came from different motives—he was headstrong, impetuous, and above all would never be beaten by animal or man. Combat was life's blood and mother's milk to him—he'd fight a seventeen two hand wild stallion bucking him to hell with as much quiet resolution as he'd court the belle of the hunt ball; he'd tame them and ride them, lifting them to unknown heights of performance, conquering them, exhausting them, loving and inspiring them. "It might be a different horse with Jonfey on its back," they'd say in the show ring or on the hunting field. "She's a different girl when she's with Jonfey," they'd say in the champagne bars. And jealously the men would utter—"They ought to leave the horses alone and geld Jonfey!"

I whispered in Jonfey's ear and he unstrapped the trench digging tool he carried on his pack. We buried the German stripped to his surprisingly clean underwear within twenty minutes. There was no requiem. The sergeant went through his pockets—pay book, identification papers, letters from home, and three tattered postcards crinkled at the edges that once had borne erotic pictures. Now they were so smudged no-one could have taken even the cheapest thrill from them.

Suddenly the sergeant gripped my arm. In the pay book was a sheet of paper, folded singly. With it was another sheet of paper on which the German had pencilled the start of what read like a request for compassionate leave. The soldier was apparently semi-illiterate, and several words had been crossed out. It was evidently his intention to make a clean copy when he had finished the composition of his first draft. I could recognise the smile that came to the sergeant's face. He had it one morning when we walked into a barrack room and found one of the lads still asleep in bed. The sergeant, smiling that smile, drew the pin on a plastic grenade, the sort that made a loud bang but do no damage, and balanced it on the side of the bed, then he walked back to the door, and shouted the man's name. The man came awake, the grenade fell to the floor and the impact exploded it. The man never overslept again.

Now he was busy writing with the stub of pencil we had found in the German's pocket. From time to time he referred to the note addressed to the German's platoon officer. When he had finished, he passed the note to me. It read, as far as I could make out in the half light, "Sir, with respect, I beg to inform you that I am tired of the war and have the intention of deserting." And it was signed with a passable imitation of the signature in the pay book. The forgery had taken only a couple of minutes. He placed the rifle conspicuously in the crook of a tree in the hedge, and rolled up the note and stuck it in the end of the barrel.

Then we set off for our first objective, a hayrick in a field over a mile away.

CHAPTER THREE

There wasn't a single building for miles around not under constant observation from the Germans. One of the reasons they continued to let the farmer occupy the farmhouse was that they could monitor his comings and goings. We had seen from aerial photographs and from the flourpaste model back in Braintree that it would be impossible to approach any of the buildings of that farm completely out of sight. And we needed a base, even for such a short stay. We also needed somewhere to erect our radio equipment. It was Jonfey who had hit on what at first seemed a hilarious plan—typical of his method of thinking and chains of thought.

"Let's set up shop in that hayrick. Build a bivvie, inside it. Have the entrance low down, there, by the hedge, and poke the aerial up through the rick itself." It was just feasible, and worked perfectly when we tried it out on a farm near Colchester. With an entire infantry platoon of the Essex Regiment borrowed for the occasion and planted around the perimeter of the field, some with field glasses, we had been able to get into the rick, set up a bivouac in its steaming belly and move freely into and out of it, unobserved.

We arrived at the rick in the corner of Hank Verhoeven's fifty-acre field just before dawn. Working in the bottom of the hedge, we withdrew the hay from the side and gradually built a hole in the centre of the rick itself, about six feet high, eight feet long, and nearly five feet wide. Most of the hay we took out via the hole, and spread it in the deep dank grass of the hedgebottom, completely out of sight. Some of it we pressed down, to make a floor on which to work. We had brought with us a mat of bamboo bars that locked together and formed a solid floor. Other bamboo sections we pushed up through the rick itself to dissipate the heat we were bound to generate. We didn't want to find ourselves at the heart of a rick fire. The job was done by ten o'clock —Jonfey got down into the hedgebottom and brewed a cup of coffee on a smokeless stove we'd brought with us. The sergeant took the first spell of duty, the rest of us spread out in the hedgebottom, Jonfey and Simon instantly went to sleep. It had been a long day, and a long night, and I could not predict when we would be able to sleep again. Certainly, once we had started, there would be little opportunity to relax. I lay down in the hedgebottom, but couldn't settle myself. It's one thing to train a group of men in the Welsh mountains, and another to take the responsibility of getting them into the German war zone and out again. Some men are born with the divine inspiration of leadership. Some men can issue a command, and without hesitation the command is obeyed. It may be the tone of the voice, a timbre bred into a man over generations. It may be the look in the eyes, the cast of a head that nobility of purpose has smiled upon. It had been my misfortune that I was abnormally fit and quick witted, and whatever task we were set I had been able to accomplish more quickly and efficiently than the average man. I applied for a commission simply because I imagined the life of an officer would be easier than that of an 'other rank'. I had no 'divine inspiration of leadership'. Nor did I strive for promotion in the Army—I had been given a Captaincy to take over this troop of men—the rank, apparently, went with the joy in the hierarchical minds of the men at the War Office—but I had no desire to be a Major, or a Lieutenant Colonel. I had always had more than enough money thanks to a prudent family line and the income from eight hundred acres of good-hearted Yorkshire farm land—but I had never owned a Rolls-Royce motor car, nor indulged myself in any of those expensive tastes that lose a heritage. I owned a couple of Purdey guns, but they came from my grandfather; my guns and the Alvis motor car had been put away for the war, wrapped in as much grease as they would support. It was very difficult for me lying in that hedge to justify, however briefly, the stewardship of the lives of the men I had brought with me.

Simon, now there was a natural officer. He should have worn the pips—not that any one of us carried any distinguishing badges of rank. Simon had the natural ease and grace that made men defer to him. Many times I'd found myself asking his advice, and then either taking it, or stubbornly and perversely cudgelling my brains to find some means, however slight, of improving on it to justify my titular superiority. But here in Holland I was in charge of a situation in which there would be no guide lines, in which I would constantly need to assess the changing dangers and order men to act accordingly. There could be no peace within me.

Jonfey woke me at eleven o'clock. I had slept the morning

through while the other three had taken turns to keep watch. There was a sour taste in my mouth, not entirely from sleeping in a hedgebottom. Jonfey had opened a couple of tins of corned beef and a packet of biscuits, and we had a hasty lunch from that and a couple of tins of cold soup. The tins we buried in a hole dug through the hay we had spread—already I had begun to feel dirty—a feeling that was to stay with me for the rest of the war. At twelve o'clock I gave the order to move and, leaving Simon behind to guard the rick, we crawled down the hedgerow, across the corner of the field, and into a small copse about half a mile north of our position. It's strange how familiar you can become with ground when you have studied aerial photographs and an accurate model. I felt I knew everything about this part of the country—could visualise it in peacetime, populated by carefree stolid Dutch people. Our brief had been thorough —Hank Verhoeven, christian name Hendrick, had lived in that farmhouse all his life. He had never married, but slept with his housekeeper who had now gone to live in Amsterdam with her married daughter, of whom Hendrick was not the father. Willem Hordenborg lived in the house behind the farm, and worked for Hendrick. He was married—his wife's name Lutte—and his three sons had gone to war. One was rumoured to be in England, one was a prisoner in Germany, and the other had been killed in action during what had erroneously been called the bloodless occupation. But we were on our way to a meeting, not with Verhoeven or Hordenborg—but a man with the unlikely name, even for Holland, of Willem Schmidt. Willem I knew all about—or as much as the Intelligence Officer in London had been able to tell me. Willem had worked before the war for a radio company in Eindhoven. He'd been something unimportant in the stores department. Now he was in command of a small detachment of the underground, the partisans, and his former managing director was one of his men. Since both shared a similar disability—Willem had lost the use of an arm, and his managing director the use of a leg, they had been drafted to work on the land. Within a half an hour they would be passing the copse in which we were hiding, with a horse-drawn cart. The managing director would be dressed in a blue denim suit, and wearing a black beret. I was now wearing the blue denim suit and black beret I had found waiting for me just inside the wood. I checked my watch. The sergeant and Jonfey had taken up positions in the small copse—I knew they were somewhere behind me, but could not see

them, so carefully had they hidden themselves. The cart was
five minutes late—five agonising minutes I spent wondering
if the whole affair was going to turn out to be a waste of time,
but then, suddenly, I heard a whistle from Jonfey somewhere
up a tree, and within a minute the cart came into sight down
the road to the north. There were no Germans about, though
in this flat country I could guess someone would have the
cart in view from any one of a dozen vantage points. The
cart came slowly towards us taking its time. The man next
to the driver slowly stretched himself, lowering the upper
part of his body back onto the load of mangels the cart carried. Then the first box was dropped gently over the side,
swung on the end of a rope, then rolled into the trough along
the side of the road, out of sight. The next box dropped
twenty yards this side, again out of sight. The managing director had the third box out on the end of its rope, swinging clear of the cart, when the motor-cycle patrol came
round the corner to the south. He dropped the box rapidly
and straightened up. The patrol halted beside the road. There
was nothing we could do. The eyes of the motorcyclist
searched the copse idly, but I was too well hidden and confident he would not see me. The man in the side-car was
holding an automatic gun between his knees, with the barrel
pointing up in the sky. For a moment I wished I had a grenade—from where I was hiding I could have put that grenade, clean as a whistle, right between his ankles. The driver
of the motor-cycle had not stopped the engine—as he sat
there he fiddled with the twist grip, revving and then letting
the engine die down. Finally, when the cart was twenty
yards from him, he revved, let in the clutch, and the combination roared past the horse and cart in a swirl of dust. The
horse showed no signs of being scared—the malicious prank
had failed. Neither Willem nor his managing director looked
around. They knew we would be watching. The motor-cycle
kept straight along the road to the corner, then disappeared
from view. We could hear the sound of its engine disappear
into the distance. There had been no pause round the corner
and no likelihood the combination passenger had jumped
out at that speed. When the cart was ten yards from me, I
prepared to move. The managing director lay back, casually,
along the load as obviously he must have done several times.
An observer watching through glasses would have felt no
surprise at seeing him do it again. This time, however, the
managing director dropped off the side of the cart as it came
level with me, and I sprang forward, low, and rolled up be-

side Willem, taking care to lie back exactly as the M.D. had done. Then I sat upright. It woud have taken an eagle's eye to see the change of places and people.

There was no time to lose in preliminaries, and Willem didn't even bother to say hello. We'd worked together in England, and would work together again, I hoped, in Holland.

"Exactly according to the plan, with one addition, they've brought another ack-ack battery and it's in Schelde, so your man will really have to fly to get you out. Today's Army net password Fluegel; code book setting, though they're not using code around here, is B Five. There's a train at Aasne, loaded with ammunition, but they're waiting for the Army to tell them when they can bring it through." He chuckled. "They can't come today because we bent the line at Boden last night. It should be repaired by two o'clock in the morning—though we're doing all we can to go slow on it. There's a list of frequencies under your seat . . ." I felt down and took the screw of paper in my hands—"with the alternatives and the frequency switch words. You're lucky—they're using diminutives today, so watch out for CHEN, LEIN, and LING." He turned, casually, and looked at me. "How are your nerves?" he asked, surprisingly.

I hadn't thought about it. How were my nerves, stranded here in Holland, with a German under every bush, and a motor-cycle combination round every bend of the road? "I think they're all right," I said. "Why do you ask?"

"Someone leaked information about that job last night. We lost four men—the Germans were waiting for us. Whoever talked about that one may know about you."

"In which case, we've had it?"

"I fear so—we might get you to the border if you want to pull out, but that's as far as we could promise. We could get you to the shore, if someone could come and pick you up. Think about it—at least they weren't waiting for you when you came down."

I told him about the boy in the hedge.

"There'd have been more than one if they'd been waiting for you and a train leaves Boden every afternoon."

"Destination, Germany?"

"Forced labour or concentration camp—take your pick."

"But you don't know yet who gave the Boden job away?"

"It was one of six men—the only six who knew about it. We'll catch him tonight or tomorrow. Shall we call it off and get you to the coast?"

"I'll think about it, and let you know later."

I rested my head on the load, and waited for the signal. The managing director should have made his way along the copse, and would be standing in position, ready to reverse the change. Suddenly I saw the broken stick on the side of the road, counted three, and rolled off the waggon. As I went down I saw the flash of denim as he nipped back onto the cart, surprisingly nimble for a man with the use of only one leg. The Germans had better not see him do that, or he'd be in a labour camp in Germany before he could say glocken-spiel.

However, I had no more time to think about him. As I went down onto the road, my hand caught a loose stone and when I rolled over, my thumb was in the wrong position. I almost screamed with pain as my thumb twisted beneath me. I rolled over and over until I was well into the depth of the copse, and slowly brought myself up under the screen of an overhanging bush. No-one was about, though I could guess Jonfey and the sergeant would not be far away, and by now would have recovered the boxes Willem had left for us. My thumb was throbbing painfully, but I was still able to move it. I tried each of the joints in turn—luckily nothing was broken, though the base of the thumb had already started to swell.

The boxes contained the local code books—God knows how Willem had managed to get hold of them—and batteries for the power pack for our radio, the key to most of my half-formed plans.

When we arrived back at the field containing the hayrick, I instructed the sergeant and Jonfey to make a special search. There was no sign of anyone in the vicinity. A woodsman born and bred to a life out of doors can tell if a field is occupied, without necessarily seeing his quarry. Many a poacher has been caught by a keeper, and never known where the keeper comes from. The birds usually give the poacher away. Birds see intruders, and either fly overhead, harried because the poacher is near a nest of young, or fly away to other fields. You will rarely catch a rabbit sitting still in a field containing a human—he might chance a run through a corner, ever alert, but he'll never sit still and wash his paws. There was a rabbit sitting in the field with the hay-rick, and a number of birds flying aimlessly about. Still, to be on the safe side, I had the sergeant and Jonfey circle the field to double check.

Simon had set up the radio in the hayrick, all except for the power pack which we carried, too heavy to have dropped with us by parachute. The power packs had been sent down five days before, in special boxes stuffed with sponge rubber and cotton wool. It didn't take more than five minutes to couple them up, and within another minute we could hear Rugby, loud and clear, and they'd opened a land-line to Braintree. The circuit was almost as clear as a telephone call. I had prepared what I wanted to say, and broadcast for less than a minute. As long as we were on 'receive' the Germans would not be able to locate us—if they could get a fix on us when we were transmitting, they could pinpoint our position to a quarter of a square mile. I can still remember clearly the answer to my urgent request for either a boat to take us off the coast of Holland, an early flight of the plane, or at least permission to change our position.

"This mission most important—urge you to forget sus-picions and complete vital life-saving task." The message had descended like a ton of bricks from the War Office to Braintree. The officer in charge of the actual operation tried to soften the blow and amplify the decision, but it still came to the same thing—stop behaving like a nervous nellie, and get on with it.

The sergeant put our feelings into words. "Of course," he said, "we could always move out and not tell them." I saw the frown flick across Simon's face—that wasn't his way at all. Jonfey, of course, didn't care one way or the other.

I don't know why I decided to stay, but the unilateral decision formed itself on my lips almost as if by its own volition. "We'll stay where we are, at least until Willem gets here this evening."

The decision once taken and expressed, all seemed anxious to forget it and get on with the job for which we'd come.

We had three radios in all. One we tuned to the company to company frequency—we could hear the individual company headquarters talking to each other, laying out the orders from the battalion commanders. It was a spasmodic traffic, mostly to do with the movement of stores. A second radio was tuned to the Divisional frequency, and yet a third to the Army. Here the traffic was heavy, and individual stations were queuing up to get into the network to pass messages.

How much the Army depends on communications. Indi-vidual groups rarely see each other, rarely mix except through the waves of the ether. Each unit, however, keeps a constant watch on the movements of all other units, and there is a certain amount of friendly backchat. What we now had to do was to establish ghost units on all those net-works—ghost units that could pass messages. Our chief difficulty, however, was the business of changing frequency, a device the Germans used to get rid of interceptors. An operator would start a message in the ordinary way, and somewhere in that message, entirely at random, he would use one of a number of code words. As soon as the receiving station heard that code word, they would know that, at the end of the current sentence or phrase, the sending station would change to an alternative frequency. The alternatives were worked out in advance and followed a pattern—luckily Willem had given me the list of alternatives, and the code words with which those alternatives would be used.

Our first opportunity came at about half past four. There had been a lively exchange since three o'clock when the commander of an Infantry company had been instructed by the battalion commander to move his entire unit to another location. In the transmission, the new location had been garbled. The sergeant, manning our receiving-transmitting set, heard the location's map reference and then heard the battalion operator sign off. By standard operating procedure, whenever a station wishes to go off the air, it says so in a certain code. For three weeks in Braintree we had learned these codes until we knew them backwards. As soon as the battalion transmitter went off the air, the sergeant smiled that smile of his. He quickly looked at the map we had spread out along one side of the hayrick, opened up his transmitter, and in a passable imitation of the battalion signaller's voice, he sent a message to the company changing the map reference. The company signaller, suspecting nothing, confirmed the new reference and went off the air. The sergeant removed his headphones, and made a circle with his thumb and finger. We had just sent an entire Infantry company fifteen miles in the direction opposite to their intended movement. I suppose our early success went to our head, because between half past four and seven o'clock we cancelled a large food order, diverted a load of ammunition from one company to another, moved two companies, put two ack-ack units on stand-down for intensive overhaul and maintenance, and instructed an entire tank unit to dump all its fuel since it was suspected of being contaminated with water. The tanks must be cleared, we insisted, since we were rushing up new fuel in the morning. Every tank had to have its carburetor stripped out completely, a job that would certainly take them all night. Once or twice we were nearly caught out when units sent supplementary signals to confirm what we had said, but by jamming the principal station and putting out a reply of our own on the alternative frequency, we were able to cover up very well. By eleven o'clock it was time to switch off our over-heated radios. It was the sergeant, however, who gave our efforts the last gorgeous coup de grace. Just before we went off the air we broadcast to each of our networks—"It is suspected that a pirate station is operating, therefore all units are ordered to ignore any instructions of whatever origin received by radio during the last twelve hours and the next six."

Then we changed frequency and called up Rugby again to report the first part of the mission completed. From now on, during the night, Rugby would broadcast on each of the frequencies we had given them, including all the alternatives, and the direction finders looking for the ghosts would track the interference back to England. No-one would suspect the damage had been done from a hayrick at the very centre of their own military machine.

Now it was time for a little field work. Willem had given me a good idea and I could see anyway that Jonfey was getting restless.

CHAPTER FOUR

Once again we left Simon in the bivouac area, but in view of the possible betrayal I suggested he take himself to the other side of the field. We had been warned the Germans have a nasty habit of dropping mortar bombs first and asking questions later, and I didn't want Simon in direct line of fire if that should happen.

"See that railway line," I said to Jonfey, handing him the map. "Take us to the nearest and safest point." To the sergeant I said I wanted to listen in to the railway communication system when I got there. He took with him a head and microphone set, an amplifier, and a small meter. The way to the railway line brought us within a thousand yards of the nearest ack-ack unit, but their sentry line was drawn close in, and from the look of them they were not set up for trouble from vagrants. The roads were busier than they had been all day—"they're obeying our movement orders," the sergeant said. I would dearly have liked to listen to the confusion of the air waves at that moment, as station to station verified the authenticity of each message received during the day. Several times we saw despatch riders—obviously all messages were being duplicated by road—lengthy procedure that should effectively do what we had set out to do —impede and delay communications. But now I had my eye on better things—a train load of ammunition.

Our journey to the railway line was slow but uneventful. We might as well have been taking a walk through the English countryside on a late summer's evening—except that half the distance we traversed on our bellies. Jonfey moved so well that half the time I didn't know where he was, though he was always close enough to come sliding up beside me whenever I indicated a halt or a pause. The sergeant and I had been together for almost a year, and with his aid I had perfected what had been little better than schoolboy German. I had learned too the habit of communicating silently with him—he seemed to spend his working life attuned somehow to my thought wavelength, and often knew my intentions before I put them into speech. We moved along slowly

across those fields together, Jonfey mostly leading, with either
the sergeant or me bringing up the rear, but whenever I
heard a suspicious sound and wanted to call a halt, the sergeant would have heard it too, and would melt into the side
of the road or the hedgebottom. Our route followed a parabola, missing the army camps, the woods, and a small inhabited hamlet. Though longer that way, I approved of Jonfey's
unusual caution. It was just after midnight when the railway
finally came into sight; again one of those clear nights, with
strong moonlight that threw every object into sheer hard
relief. You get the impression you can see for miles, and
distances travelled are therefore shorter. It was a cool evening, cool on the skin without the fall of dew that makes
everything heavy with moisture. It's hard to say whether
we were affected by where we were, and what we were doing.
Certainly within myself I felt that quiet excitement I had
last known prior to examinations—the awesome secret fear
of failure that is stifled by the rational appraisal of your conscious abilities. "I can do it," you say silently to yourself, "I
can do it." It's one of those seventy-five per cent confidences
—"I can do it, the way I now feel, or if nothing happens
that I have not been able to predict, or if things go my way,
or . . ." There are a thousand 'ors' as tempting as the song
of the Lorelei and as fatal. We walked along the railway
line until we came to a small cutting. For no reason, the land-
scape had suddenly pimpled, and where the pimple came, a
road crossed the railway. It was a road not frequently in use
—more of a track I saw when I examined its surface. Certainly no vehicle had been down there for many a long day.
We walked into the tunnel in the cutting and found, as we
had expected, two small recesses in the wall along which
the signals cables passed. The recesses were designed for two
men to take shelter should a train catch them in the small
tunnel; the three of us squeezed into one like sardines. After
we had been there a little while I sent Jonfey back out again
to observe the end of the tunnel. I didn't think anyone had
seen us coming in, but I was taking no chances. The sergeant,
meanwhile, isolated the wire along which the Meldenkirche
to Aasne messages were sent, scraped bare the insulation and
clamped on his terminals. Now he could overhear anything
said down that line, and sat there, headphones on his head
and microphone dangling below his mouth, like the telephone
operator of a London hotel. One thing is certain, his reaction
to the calls would be a damned sight swifter than the service
I had been used to. But then, he didn't have his knitting,
cups of tea, or frequent calls from his loved one to contend

with. Nor was he sitting with his shoes off and his toes wriggling into the thick pile of a hotel carpet—he was halfway
up a dark tunnel, down the inside walls of which water had
been dripping, to judge by the rancid smell, for a thousand
years. Rats moved along the bottom of the walls, and occasionally I caught the gleam of their baleful eyes. The alcove into which we had tucked ourselves was particularly
nauseating, since a linesman or some other itinerant at some
time in the past had dropped his trousers to relieve himself
in there. Jonfey had trodden in it, and that didn't help matters. Suddenly, I became aware again of the little irritations
—my thumb was hurting like hell, my shirt was wet and
sticking to me, I had dirty hands and that always has annoyed me, but above all I hadn't had sufficient food and sleep
in the last twenty-four hours. There's a small place hidden
somewhere inside yourself to which you go to lick your
wounds. From the outside you appear normally active, normally attentive to what is going about you—but inside, the
little you is squatting in its corner, bathed in self-pity. God,
how I hated the Army, and the life it forced me to lead. I
took the spare pair of headphones from my top pocket, and
the sergeant taped them on to the wires with his own. He
had been listening to the voices, his lips moving as he tried
to memorise them. This was what they must have sounded
like to Joan of Arc, or to the fixated inmates of lunatic asylums. There we were squatting in that dark hole, amidst the
overpowering odour of freshly disturbed faeces, listening to
the well-scrubbed voices of the bright individuals of the
world beyond, the world of supper breaks, and stoves in
railway signalling boxes, and clean white paper to write on,
and neat lines of responsibility and, most important of all,
somewhere someone in command to whom you could refer
all decisions. Most of the calls were longer distance than interested us, most concerning the railhead at Oistbeeck.
Most of the messages concerned routine movements of passenger and goods trains. Much of it was the movement of
goods of one sort or another. But all the messages contained
that damned note of cleaned humanity—"load of coal coming up for you, Sinderquist, so you'll be able to keep your
stove warm." "What do you suppose they want with fifty
tons of sugar—anyway, one of the bags had burst so we've
pulled it off at Aasne, so you can make your tally board accordingly—we'll be having sweet coffee tonight, that I can
tell you." And the maddening reply—"Go on, you won't see
coffee until the morning—you'll be drinking the beer and
schnapps that accidentally got broken on their way through

Aasne last Tuesday!" Last Tuesday. Already it was vintage. I would have given several unimportant pieces of my aching anatomy for a glass of beer laced with schnapps, at that moment!

Then came the message for which we had waited. From Aasne. To movement control at Meldenkirche. Amidst the military jargon, the message was clear. "How are they getting on with the line at Boden, and when may we bring the train through?" Boden was not on the main route to Oistbeeck—it would take a simple change of points to connect the main line with the Boden line. Next stop after Boden was Meldenkirche, the nearest point to the military encampment. Meldenkirche told Aasne they would ring them back in about ten minutes. In five minutes the sergeant had cut the signal line neatly in two, and was operating both sides of it. The message came back in eight minutes, but by then the sergeant was ready, and assuming the accent of the Aasne operator, he took the message from Meldenkirche— "The train cannot move tonight—there has been difficulty with the repair, and the branch line is not expected to be opened before the morning. Over and out." Then the sergeant switched his tapping, and rang the Aasne operator.

"Meldenkirche here," the sergeant said, when the telephone was lifted at the other end.

"Yes."

"About your message—04/07/55."

"Damn it, I've lost my pad. Which message was that?"

"Your last one, about the special train."

"Oh that—well, can we get rid of it? It's making us nervous here. Of course we're not supposed to know what's in it, but everyone is certain it is full of dangerous high explosives."

"So it is! Well, you'll be happy to know the line is mended, so you can send the train through any time. Get your main line movement from Oistbeeck, and send it through."

"Who'll do the signalling?"

"You'll do it from your end. The signalling system is down at Boden, of course, and so you'll have to tell the driver to ignore signals once he's along the Meldenkirche line—we can't fix the signalling system tonight."

"You've got a bit of a cold or something, haven't you, Arnot?" I looked at the sergeant. Certainly, his voice was a stage lower than the operator at Meldenkirche, but I had thought his imitation very good. However, the two operators must have known each other for a lifetime, and it was setting a difficult task to hope to imitate someone you've heard only a few minutes.

"Ja, it's my sinus trouble again!" the sergeant said. He was lucky—his blind shot had hit the bull.

"Well, you always did have trouble with the sinus, didn't you. Take care of yourself and we'll push it through from here."

"Good night then."

"Good night? We shall be talking again later. What about our chess game?" The sergeant uttered a silent curse. I could almost hear his mind tick over. I made a sign with my thumb over my arm and he understood immediately.

"We shan't be able to play tonight," he said. "I have to go for an injection for my sinus, and you know how that makes me sleepy. Remember last year?" Such is the power of auto-suggestion, the man in Aasne chuckled.

"Don't I just remember," he said. "That was the night I got a fool's mate. Well, take care, and I'll speak with you tomorrow."

It took us a half an hour to fasten explosive charges to the railway line, about fifty feet from the Aasne end of the tunnel, and to tamp the explosive charge with earth and gravel to suppress the noise the explosive would make. We had brought with us gun-cotton slabs and tied three to each line. One slab was to be the cutting charge, the other two destined to turn the cut end of the line through a slight angle; an angle not steep enough to be seen, but which would derail the oncoming train as easily and as certainly as if the railway line had come to an abrupt end. Gun-cotton is not a noisy explosive, fortunately, especially when its major force, as in this case, was being directed downwards. We selected a piece of the line between sleepers and scooped out as much gravel as we could with our hands and with the trenching tool. Then came the truly dangerous business of crimping and attaching the detonators, which the sergeant carried suspended on elastic bands inside a tin lined with cotton wool. For detonators we were using small tubes about as long as a Swan Vestas match which fit over the end of the thin fuse rope. However, to ensure a perfect fit, the fuse rope has to be slid inside the detonator tube, which must then be crimped onto the rope. The only satisfactory way to do this, without elaborate instruments, is to put the detonator in your mouth, and crimp round the soft metal end with your teeth. If you crimp in the wrong place, the detonator contains sufficient explosive power to blow off the top of your head. Some people cannot bear to put the detonator inside their mouths and crimp them from the side, but my philosophy has always been, 'in for a penny, in for a pound', and your head would get blown off wherever you put the detonator, inside or out. It's strange to watch the face of a man crimping a detonator. When he puts it inside his mouth he has a sickly look of total concentration, as if convinced he will vomit; he measures the position of the end of the tube blindly with his fingers, and usually readjusts the detonator's position. I have seen few men who can put one in and crimp it first time. Then you can see him making up his mind to do it, ordering his jaws to close so that his teeth press on the soft tube. Some men fail at this point—I have known normally brave men whose jaws have locked open with a detonator inside. Finally, however, most men acquire from somewhere the fortitude to close their jaws on the soft metal. It tastes horrible. And then you press, gently, turn the detonator through ninety degrees and do the job over again, with the same reactions. Crimping detonators is not like performing any other dangerous feat—when you've crossed the barrier of fear once it's usually not difficult to cross it again, to act to an unfeeling pattern that itself suppresses the feeling of danger. But every detonator you crimp is a new detonator. It doesn't help that no-one will ever sit near someone who is crimping detonators—not, I imagine, from a feeling of self-preservation but because they wish to evade the horror of being close if one goes off. It's a lonely, disgusting, fear-raddled job.

One of the hardest things about being an officer is the need, sometimes, to look beyond immediate reality, to see what is glibly known as 'the overall picture', and to realise that one has overriding responsibilities. To many men it must seem like cowardice when officers hand over dangerous jobs—possibly in some cases fear and cowardice are the strongest forces. I handed the detonators and the fuse cord to Jonfey. He half smiled at me, and at the sergeant. He could accept that he was the most expendable of the three of us, but neither he nor I nor the sergeant liked stating the thought. This was playing it by the book, and no mistake. I would not do him the disservice of dressing it up in false flattery—"Here, Jonfey, you're best at this job." That would convince no-one. He took the detonators and fuse cords, and walked twenty feet down the line. Then he sat as close to the bank as he could get, facing away from us, protecting us in the event of a failure with his own body. In the set of his hunched shoulders I could feel his silent protest—"I can play it by the book, too." Possibly I was oversensitive—it's not a comforting thing to give a man a task you yourself can do as well as he can, knowing a mistake will kill him. That's something the men who write the manuals might care to remember—though I can see the need for doing things by the book, even with a bunch of pirates as comic as our special services. But I've often wondered, in a boat at sea, with the food and water supply having run out, who should go overboard—a husband, his wife, or his children. Most men, by-the-book heroes, would jump overboard first. Most wives would follow unthinkingly. What a tragedy it could be if the children turned out wrong or couldn't carry on surviving because they lacked the adults' experience, knowledge and fortitude.

When the detonator has been crimped, there is a look that comes on the face, the blanched white edges of the mouth suffuse with the blood of relief, and the whole personality is affected by arrogant success. Jonfey handed the detonators on their fuses to the sergeant, who inserted them into the gun-cotton blocks and taped them secure. Then we started carefully to tamp the blocks, to deaden the sound as much as possible. A half an hour later, the charge was ready for blowing. We retreated over the edge of the cutting and waited. The sergeant could sense my dilemma—do we blow the rails now, and run the risk the explosion will be heard and the train stopped, or do we wait until the train comes. The train itself would be guarded, and we would need to be close to the line to activate the explosion—at least, one of us would need to be there. The chances of escape were slender—either the explosion of the train would get you, or the guards most certainly would if they survived. Decisions, decisions! "Blow it!" I said. The sergeant lit his fuse cord match and applied it to the end of the fuse, and then we left, down the embankment, along the edge of the field as fast as possible. We had got a half mile away and I was watching the seconds hand on my watch when suddenly we heard a distant crump. I looked up in surprise—the railway wasn't due to go for at least another forty-five seconds. But then, suddenly I realised the crump had been repeated, and suddenly there was a whole salvo of crumps, but on the far side of Meldenkirche. The 'action in force', whatever it was, had started.

The salvo was at its height when our tiny explosion went off—a mere snuffle of sound that would have been lost in the general holocaust had I not been looking at the seconds sweep of my watch. Confident now that our explosion would have alerted no-one, we turned and went back to the line. The rails had been severed neatly, and the ends pushed about twelve inches to the side. The train, coming down the

line at speed, would leave the track and smack straight into
the back of the tunnel. We walked and crawled to a position
about a mile from the railway and hardly had time to eat
our bully-beef and biscuits supper, washed down with water
from a brook and glucose and vitamin-strong lemonade
powder, when the train came rumbling along the line. All
its lights were out and it was doing at least sixty miles
an hour. There was an awesome screech as it hit the bent
rail, and white-hot sparks flew up into the night as the
wheels left the track and the train started to slither along
the gravel of the permanent way. Then there seemed to be
a silent pause, but only for a second, before the whole of
the thundering train banged into the side of the tunnel
mouth. In that cutting there was nowhere else for the trucks
to go but forwards—the whole train concertinaed on itself,
and there was a sudden crack. I had no need to cry 'down'
—both the sergeant and Jonfey pushed their faces to the
ground the moment they heard it. And then the bulk of the
explosive went off, in one air-shattering bang so loud it
numbed every sense in the body, despite my hands clapped
over my ears. It was a noise so full and complete it seemed
to enter through the bones of the body, and then the shock
wave came, and with it the tearing splintering jerking sounds
as tree trunks were snapped like leg bones, and gravel and
timber and glass and steel bars and truck sides bansheed
through the air. The tongue of flame from the train shot up
high as a hill, red flame with an incredibly yellow and white
centre, and very little smoke.

And then it all started to come down again, screeching
through the air, with a sudden back lash of wind into the
heart of the explosion.

Jonfey was slapping the sergeant on the back. He would
have liked to slap my shoulder, that I knew, but discipline
prevailed. I slapped his shoulder, but that was quite permis-
sible in the circumstances.

I'd never blown up a train before. I messed about on the
ranges at Warminster with the burned-out hulks of old tanks,
but somehow it wasn't the same, it wasn't the same. I didn't
even mind that there had been human beings on that train,
and that they must have perished with it. They were part of
the anonymous black evil of the enemy—my purpose in life,
which I had accepted completely the day I put on uniform,
was to kill as many of them as possible. With no regrets. Kill
or be killed! Fight for freedom! Save our way of life. You're
doing it for the country, for the mothers, for the unborn
babies, for England, St. George, and all that crap. You're

doing it—and for Christ's sake, stop asking why. Self-sacrifice doesn't have to be in public, with nails through the palm of your hand, and you don't have to walk up the hill with a plank on your shoulder. You can do it, lying on your belly in a stinking field, crimping bits of aluminium between your teeth that probably need cleaning anyway. You do it when, where, and as you are.

I was crying. Oh, there weren't any tears I couldn't explain away—the shock of the explosion, happiness, relief—but inside me I was crying for the dead men, all the victims of the war, the little man with three dirty postcards in his pockets and his life's blood bubbling up out of his throat where I'd stuck the knife. Truly I meant to get his hands—but it never matters what you mean to do, does it? What happens is the evidence on which you are tried and judged, not what you mean to do.

The sergeant saw the tears, but neither one of us could speak about them.

We crouched under the hedgerow, and moved fast.

I had to talk to Rugby.

CHAPTER FIVE

When we returned to the bivouac in the field containing the hayrick, two things had happened. Simon had prudently reinstalled inside a five-tree copse at the bottom of a field of wheat, and we had had visitors. German, of course, and their calling cards burned the hayrick to the ground and made a hole three feet deep. The stench of burning hay alerted us, but we went into the twenty acre to make certain. The Germans left four men to watch for our possible return, but evading them was easier than our training had implied— each of the four must have been a townie from the slabbed pavements of Hamburg or Munich with as much idea of concealment as a tart on her long-awaited honeymoon. Two of them, incredible though it may seem, were smoking. I felt like giving them a medal and seven days confined to barracks. One of them had apparently heard about the great outdoors, and was sitting in a hedgebottom. Unfortunately his legs were sticking out, and his boots were size ten, all of them showing. Where is the Master race—where the copybook soldiers we've heard so much about? We left them guarding the field and the empty smoking remains of a hole in the ground, and went to look for Simon. I don't know why, but automatically I assumed these clodhoppers would not have caught him! We had planned, in Braintree, Essex, a 'get-together' technique for just such an occasion as this. We left the hayrick behind us, and travelled a distance of a thousand feet. Then we found the nearest place of safety and Jonfey sat there. He'd earned himself a rest. The sergeant and I both started out along the perimeter of a circle whose radius was a thousand feet, and whose centre was the hayrick, our previous position. I had travelled only five hundred yards, when I saw Simon. He was up a tree, a high chestnut. It was a bird that gave him away. At that time of night, birds are supposed to be asleep. This one wasn't. Simon was sitting deliberately close to its nest. The signals equipment was festooned throughout the tree, invisible from the ground below in the dense foliage. Once I had identified him, I went back and waited with Jonfey. The sergeant scouted a thousand yards, as we had planned, approximately half way round a circle of radius a thousand feet, and then returned. He was walking in an anti-clockwise direction—the clockwise man by our method would walk round the entire circle. If that hadn't worked, we would have increased the radius to fifteen hundred feet, and repeated the procedure. It's the only safe method of finding a man once you've become separated, other than him laying a hounds and hares trail of broken twigs. The Germans too can follow broken twigs—anything you can see, it's a safe bet they can see just as quickly.

We settled like partridges in the tree—there was room for half a platoon up there, and opened up the call to Rugby. The reception again was very good, but I didn't dare stay on 'transmit' for too long. The gist of my message was to ask if the plane flying in to lift us out could come as soon after first light as possible—our mission was accomplished and if we were known to be in the vicinity, the Germans could not avoid finding us. The noise of the battle beyond Meldenkirche was muted now, and I assumed a rearguard action was being fought by a few unfortunate sods delegated to take care of the mopping up.

Rugby put me through to Braintree, who got busy on the telephone presumably to the War Office and the Air Ministry and the Met Office—and the pick-up was arranged for eight o'clock, in four hours time. By then it would be light, but we'd all have to take our chances. By now it was four o'clock and I was whacked. We stripped the radio equipment apart and hid it more carefully in the branches. I wasn't going to bother to cart that all the way back to England with me—anyway, Willem, I felt certain, could make good use of it. About half past four I climbed down the tree to look about me and to urinate—I didn't feel like exposing myself in front of the men—a stupid prudery I've never escaped since my days of communal wash-rooms at public school. The actual lavatories, with half doors over which supervising prefects could peer without warning, theoretically to reduce the incidence of masturbation but in practice to make disparaging remarks about the size of your manhood had had a great effect upon me—so great that during my entire education and for years afterwards I was in a state of perpetual constipation in danger of becoming addicted to senna pods.

The tree was easier to climb down than to climb up—almost gaily I jumped the last six feet.

They were waiting for us. All round the copse. The Germans I mean.

CHAPTER SIX

They were about fifty and most had automatic weapons, machine guns hand-held to spit a death a second. Not the slovenly soldiers left to baby-sit a vacated hayrick, these were the military Herrenvolk, efficient killers trained to get close silently, quickly, completely unobserved. Up that tree I had more field-craft talent than the rest of the British Army —the Germans ran through our observation like water through a sieve; anyone can do it from ground level, if they put their minds to it, but only a trained expert can sneak up on men at a height of twenty feet or more. The German officer made a silent hand signal and the automatic weapons were lifted skywards. Horrified I watched them squeeze the triggers, the noise appalling as they hosed the tree with lead, twigs and branches and leaves flying in the fastest pruning I'd ever seen. When the burst ended the rifles were lowered as one, with no order spoken.

It's not good to think you've been responsible for the deaths of three men by stupidity. I ought to have posted Jonfey at least five hundred yards from the tree to give warning—but arrogantly assumed that at height, observing in all directions, it would be impossible for anyone to approach us unseen. Lesson number one in this practical demonstration of my inabilities—don't put all your eggs in one basket. My mind numbly refused to accept the meaning of the scene my eyes had just witnessed. I thought of a silly joke someone had told me about a man who filled a bullring with Spaniards—when a riot came he was held responsible since he had put all his 'basques in one exit'. A giggle at the appalling joke drew thin bitter saliva to my mouth. The grasshopper flick of memory was of course the safety valve for a psychological head of fear. The giggle burst uncontrollably from me, my shoulders shook with shame and soon I was laughing without control and the laugh would have turned into wracking sobs, but the sergeant, Jonfey and Simon climbed unharmed out of the tree. The gunners had aimed only at the tree's edges, deliberately avoiding its heart. It was a warning, no more, that this was the SS, and they wanted us alive. Not infantry butchers dedicated, as we ourselves were, to destroying the body of the enemy, these men saw us as a potential source of information. The officer incharge beckoned, and the men formed a square about us, heading eastwards. As we started to march away, the last rank of men climbed the tree, and soon we could hear the crash of radio equipment being thrown down. At the end of the wheat field parked on a small service road was a truck, with a large metallic ring above it. The flat side of the ring pointed at the tree. Behind the truck two lorries had benches for soldiers. The sergeant and Simon went into the first lorry, Jonfey and I into the second. The officer came to sit beside me as the convoy drove away.

"What is your name?" he asked me, a pleasant conversational opening gambit.

I didn't speak. Next, I felt, he should ask, "Do you come here often?"

"No matter. I'll find out when we get to barracks."

He took a silver cigarette case from the top pocket of his tunic. In it he had Players cigarettes. He saw me looking at them, and offered one to me. Significantly, he didn't offer one to Jonfey. How on earth did he know I was in command of our party? I looked quickly down over my uniform. I had stripped completely before starting on this job, and had drawn all my clothing and equipment alongside the rest of them to make quite certain I was clad no differently from them.

"How did you catch us?" I asked, as much to stop him asking questions as to acquire information, though I was burning to know what had given us away.

"We knew you were not far away," he said blandly. "Willem told us that." Steady, now, he could be trying to trap you when he talks about Willem—and there could be other Willems than Willem Schmidt.

"Who's Willem?"

"Ah, so you're going to be naïve. Good, that helps. It is always easier to break a man when he tries to be naïve and clever at the same time. We had the frequency for your calls to Rugby and your control, and luckily three detector vans in the neighbourhood. It was just a question of waiting until you started to broadcast on that frequency, and drawing three straight lines on a map. They crossed exactly at that copse." Damn, so it was Willem Schmidt! Only he had the Rugby frequency, for use in emergency. Well, this was the emergency all right, but it was apparent Willem wouldn't be doing any broadcasting.

"Don't worry about Rugby," the officer continued, "we've

taken a leaf from your book and broadcast to tell them to
ignore any further signals that may be sent. That was a
clever trick of yours, telling the Army network a spy had
been operating—it threw messages into suspicion sent days
ago. And just so you won't feel too badly, it put us into such
chaos that your friends over the other side of Meldenkirche
got completely away. We caught only five prisoners, sick and
elderly Jews who had volunteered to stay."

This man amazed me. I would estimate he was just over
thirty years of age, compared to my thirty-two, but he had
an older blandness about him I couldn't comprehend. In his
circumstance I would have been crowing at capturing four
prisoners, or so angry I would be tempted to use physical
violence! As tall as I was, he certainly looked as fit—not at
all the sort of man I would want to tangle with in personal
combat without the wartime licence of knives and razor
blades and the paraphernalia of legalised skullduggery with
which we had trained. I had worked my body slightly forwards on the seat and only Jonfey had seen the movement.
My chance came on a corner when the man on my side of
the truck suddenly were thrown off balance. Awaiting such
a moment as I went forward I had twisted to the side, right
leg back and left leg forward. As the truck got into the turn
my weight eased forward and I was in the natural position
to vault over the tailboard. I saw Jonfey through the corner
of my eye start to rise after me, but the weight of the turn
was keeping him off balance and I doubted he would make
it. I put my right hand on the tailboard—the pain from my
thrumb was excruciating but there was no time to react to it.
As my body went forward my arm took the weight and my
legs came up and I slid over the tailboard to the right. I
heard the shout start as I hit the ground and rolled instantly
over towards the side of the road. Jonfey too had made it
over the tailboard and came after me. The roll ended with
me sitting at the side of the road leaning to go through the
hedge. I dived straight into it head first. A brick wall had
been built there, masked by the brush.

I recovered back in the truck, wired to one of the up-
rights supporting the canvas roof. Jonfey lying on the floor
of the truck had blood oozing from his side.

"He got over the wall," the officer said, seeing the direction of my look—"so we had to shoot him. It's only a flesh
wound, of course; we wouldn't want to hurt him. I can see
you have been trained very well," he said, eyeing me with
respect. "We shall have to be more careful with you. It's a
pity about the wall, if it hadn't been there I think you would

have got away!" Again that bland admiration, cool appraisal. If this was to be the interrogating officer, God help us. I shivered. In my post-concussive clarity, his coolness seemed the bloodless venom of a snake man.

The trucks slowed down, turned left, and I could see over the tailboard the shape of a guard house. It had once been a greenhouse, the glass now replaced by black canvas. We drove up a well-used track, and the lorry halted. We were outside an enormous house, almost large enough to be a castle. Rooms on five floors, and doubtless there were cellars. Parked in a conspicuous position in front of the house, on a square of what once had been lawn, was a row of ambulances. At least they looked like ambulances, but from this distance I could see them without engines, wooden constructions shaped and painted to stimulate ambulances. How like the SS to camouflage their headquarters as a hospital to avoid bombardment from the air by stupidly sentimental Englishmen.

There was nothing hospital-like about the interior. The house had been converted into a beehive of officialdom, with signboards crudely fixed everywhere. The doors had been hand carved in mahogany, but the Germans had no thought of preserving the fabric when they went around it with hammers and nails. In the room into which we were taken was what had been an Aubusson carpet before the hob-nailed soldiery stomped its pile to ribbons. Across one corner of the room a gorgeous table was now used as a desk. I looked about me. This whole room in its heyday before the war had been styled in the French Empire tradition as a salon. The Germans had not even bothered to empty it of its elegant contents, but were making the best use of it as it stood. The effect it had on me was the same as I once experienced in a hotel in York, when a titled lady, whose name I would not divulge, suddenly lost her topless evening gown as she walked in to dinner. It was one of those dreadful accidents that can happen to any woman. She stood regally there, surrounded by her precious garments in disarray. There was no vulgarity, no titillation of the senses, no thought of a free peepshow, though the heat of the evening had caused her to wear what in those days was scanty underwear. Haughty, proud, though disarrayed, she had but to array herself again. When the Germans had gone, the room would array itself again, it had the proportions, the atmosphere of quiet composure, the dignity.

I was forcing myself to concentrate on this recondite matter only because I did not want to think of the immediate future. I would be questioned, and possibly reprisals would be taken against my person for what we had achieved. That was the natural order of this eye-for-an-eye war, and I was prepared for that. You take part in any illegal activity with full expectation of retribution, even though you may fool yourself you have licence for your actions. Brought up as I was to the natural life of seasons of the countryside, you realise no-one can pervert the natural order without retribution. Governments do this with their artificial summer time, councils change the course of rivers to make housing estates, city-bred men spray city-made chemicals on the ground, all setting themselves against the natural order. Some time or another, sure as God made eggs, there's an accounting—national milk yield is down, soil is eroded, and virulent pests who eat chemicals, and live, abound. There has to be an accounting at some time or another.

I was prepared for the accounting. Seven days bread and water? A flogging? Shooting; even, I believe, death. But I wasn't prepared for any deviation of the natural expression of the wish to punish—I wasn't prepared, for example, for torture. How in hell do you prepare yourself for torture, short of pulling out all your toe and finger nails in advance? To be quite honest—I was scared—just plain scared.

The four of us were paraded in that room, photographed, had our fingerprints taken and our pockets emptied—though I managed to keep my wrist watch—and were marched to the top of the building and locked in what had been a maid's bedroom. It measured ten feet by ten feet and still contained a brass bedstead with a mattress but no bedding, a wash stand without ewer or bowl, a couple of pictures on the wall, framed postcards of the kind they used to give out for regular attendance at Sunday School. The glass of one picture had been broken and removed. We waited until the guard had locked the door, and the sergeant quickly removed the glass from the other picture. He took off his jacket and wrapped the glass inside it. Then he snapped the glass into pieces.

One sliver he gave to each of us, the remains he tucked into the mattress for possible future use. My piece was about three inches long, a half an inch wide, murderously pointed. I ripped one of the belt tabs from the side of my trousers, and unpicked the stitching across the end. The belt tab, sewn double could now be opened at the end like a finger stall and was about two inches deep to the button hole. It made a useful glove for the flat end of the glass sliver, a handy sheath that would prevent the glass cutting my hand should I have occasion to use it. Each man hid his glass sliver in a different place. The sergeant used his to slice the underside of his denim collar. He then worked the glass through the slit. With his hands behind his head he would be able to pluck that glass from under his collar and throw it. The boys told me the sergeant could score double twenty with a throwing knife any time he wished. Simon put his in a pleat of his denim jacket where it was stitched into the cuff—the boys in the infantry used to press these pleats with a hot iron to make the jacket parade worthy. Jonfey, trust him, put his inside the covering flap of his fly. We couldn't suppress a small laugh. "Well," he said, with pretended truculence. "It's the most natural thing in the world to go for your knob, isn't it?" We had to admit there was justification in what he said. A pouch at the back of the denim jacket covers the button holes where the jacket buttons to the trousers. I hid my glass sliver in that pouch and felt much better. Barely had I done so when there were footsteps along the corridor, and the door was unlocked. A medical orderly came into the room, alone, with a wooden box of first aid kit. He asked Jonfey to lie down on the bed and opened his battledress and lifted his shirt and vest. The wound was apparently clean, and the bullet had passed through the flesh at Jonfey's waist, missing the bones. The orderly dusted the wound with a white powder and stuck a plaster over it. He then gave Jonfey two pills from a bottle. Jonfey looked at me and I shook my head from side to side. The orderly gave Jonfey a small glass of water from a bottle in the first aid kit—Jonfey looked at me and I nodded. He put the tablets in his mouth and drank the water. Then he had a spasm of coughing, and took his handkerchief to his mouth. When he had stopped coughing he looked at me and winked. The tablets were in the handkerchief. Better the pain in his side, unpleasant though it may be, than two unknown drugs which might, or might not, be simple aspirins. Anyway, I had genuine morphine tablets sewn into the linings of my pocket. As soon as the orderly had gone, I took a morphine tablet from my pocket and gave it to Jonfey. He lay back on the bed, and within a couple of minutes, the pain had started to ease. The wound was not serious, and we could effectively forget about it. "We'll be interrogated separately," I said, remembering the warning Braintree had given us about the possibility of concealed microphones if we were locked together in one small room. "But I don't want any heroes. Tell them everything you know, and don't make up any funny stories."

"Do you mean that!" Jonfey asked. "Can't we have them on a bit of string?"

"No we can't, or they'll have us on a bit of string—but theirs will be tied around the ends of your thumbs."

"Do we tell them where we have come from?" Simon asked.

"Yes, you can tell them we came from an airport just outside Canterbury. I don't imagine that will do the slightest harm, since once Control realise they've lost us, they'll shut up shop and open up elsewhere."

"But can't we make up a story for them?" Jonfey was determined to have his last fling of defiance.

"No you can't. The most you can do is to make them ask you a question for every fact they want to know. Don't volunteer any information, but if they ask a direct question, answer it. I don't want anyone coming out of this place with a broken body—remember, these boys are experts at interrogation—they've had the Jews to practise on for a good number of years. Tell them what they want to know, and with luck you'll go to prisoner-of-war camps, and sit out the rest of the war. Try to be funny, and there won't be enough of you left to bury. And that, lads, is my last order."

I could see they didn't like it, Jonfey in particular was furious. I don't really think he was mad at being captured —after all, anyone can be thrown at a fence. But it was not being able to mount again and ride on that bothered him. The sergeant hated the Germans more than any of us—we'd all spent some time in Germany before the war—Simon had studied for a year at Goettingen as part of his veterinary course, and Jonfey had show-jumped in Munich, Hamburg, Berlin and several other places. But the sergeant had lived among them—had even been taken as a German by his neighbours and the people who worked alongside him—and he had seen the rise to power of the Hitler-inspired SS machine. He'd witnessed the persecutions at close quarters, and had come into the Army with a personal grudge. He never said anything about it, but one night when we celebrated the end of a long spell of training by sharing a bottle of Naafi whisky in the hills beneath Cader Idris, I asked him why he hadn't married. We had a good fire going in a gap between two hills. The boys had knocked off a sheep, and we had cooked a part of it as a stew—there are few tastes to beat that of fresh mutton stew, with potatoes and carrots, and the fresh wild thyme that grows among the rocks of the Welsh hills. The bottle had sunk to the last inch, and we knew the euphoria of fresh air, the outdoors, food, whisky, and the end of training.

"How is it you've never married, sergeant?"

"If I might be personal, sir, I could ask you the same question."

"In my case, it's very simple—I've never met a girl I liked sufficiently to want to ask her to marry me!"

"I knew a girl, in Germany in 1936. I'd been living up in Bergen, working on the fishing boats—only a lad of course."

He would have been twenty-one in 1936 and already, as I knew from previous conversations, had traversed Russia on the bum. "I came down into the Ruhr to get a job—men were making a fortune in the steel works at that time. I got myself a little place in a very small hotel run by a very nice family called Rosenberg. They didn't have many guests staying there—you can guess why from the name, I imagine. Well, this family had a daughter, and I fell for her like a ton of bricks. Of course, that didn't suit my plans at all—I intended to make a pile and leave Europe for America, Canada, the West. In those days, there was something magnetic about the West."

"What about Miss Rosenberg?"

"Well, she was getting a bit stuck on me, so I thought I'd better cool her off a bit. Anyway, the way things were going in Germany, once I'd made my pile I intended to get out of there, p.d.q. Then one night after supper, old man Rosenberg came to my room and more or less popped the question on behalf of his daughter. Would I marry her and take her with me? He'd give me his entire savings."

"And did you?"

"Honestly, sir, I couldn't. It's not that she wasn't a smasher all right—as lovely a girl as I'd ever known, and such a sweetness with it I'd never laid my hands on her. Honest! I never even touched her. But you see, it meant death to me, the very idea of marriage. I'd always been a runner. I ran away from home and school at fourteen, and never stopped once. I couldn't bear the idea of settling in one place. Of course, I know why—I was running away from my old Dad—old Do-it-all, we used to call him at home. He never believed anyone other than himself could do anything. Do you know, sir, he even used to cook the Sunday dinner, and my Mam standing by looking at him, idle!"

We each took a drink of whisky, and I brought him back to the girl. "About five nights after her old Dad made me the offer I was in my room, starting to pack. A couple of shirts and a spare suit was about the total of it, but having turned the daughter down, I had to get out of there. The folks had gone to bed, and a little night man who used to come on duty at ten and sleep in the office downstairs had already arrived, and suddenly I heard this tap on the door. The door opened and in she walked. She was wearing a dressing gown I reckon must have been her Dad's because it fastened the wrong way. It's funny how you notice that sort of thing when you're all worked up, isn't it? And was I worked up! I'd had girls in dressing gowns in my room before—there was one at Bergen would come every night if I'd let her. But not this one. As I told you, I'd never laid hands on her. And she sits down on the edge of the bed, and then she asks me. 'You're going away, aren't you?' I had to tell her. 'And it's because of what Father asked you?' I had to admit it, and tried to tell her it wasn't any failing on her part. That when I was good and ready, she was exactly the kind of gal I'd be looking for, and I'd keep a picture of her always in my heart and all that sort of stuff, and then she started to cry, but it wasn't what I thought. 'Is it difficult to make a baby?' she asked me, just like that. 'Are you in trouble?' I asked her. I was flabbergasted. You know how it is—well, perhaps you don't know, sir, how it is, but I imagined that because *I'd* never touched her she was pure, and no-one else had ever touched her. I remember thinking what a laugh it would be if all the time I was keeping hands off some local German lad was having it nightly and twice on Sunday. And then it all came out. If I wouldn't marry her, would I at least give her a baby? Of course, I was flattered— but it wasn't the image of me she wanted—it was the pregnancy she could get the local doctor to stamp on a card to get out of the country. At that time, the only Jews they were letting out were pregnant mothers whose husbands were abroad."

I fuelled the fire again with logs the boys had cut before they went down to Aberdovey for a night out. I tipped the last of the whisky bottle into the sergeant's mug, and opened a fresh bottle. I knew we'd finish both bottles that night. I didn't want to hear the rest of his story—but I knew I must.

"To cut a long story short," he said, "I let her stay in my bed that night, and about three o'clock in the morning, when we were both half asleep, it happened. She was so happy the next morning. I left the digs feeling bloody horrible. Five months later I'd made a pile of money, but the political thing was coming to the boil and Germany was no place for me. I went back to the hotel to ask her to marry me and come with me. Some bugger had been there before me and burned the hotel to the ground with the Rosenbergs and my kid in it."

Most of us were fighting for children everywhere—the

sergeant was fighting for one unborn child and all the mothers of the world.

"When do you think they'll start the interrogation?" Simon asked, quietly.

"I imagine they'll leave us here for quite a while—part of the psychological treatment to wear down our nerves."

"What do you suggest we do to pass away the time?"

"Nothing planned. I don't agree with the idea of running away from things, even mentally. We've all got to face the fact that we have an ordeal to go through, and if we face up to it, when it comes we will be better equipped to deal with it. We can sleep a little, if that's possible, but for the rest of the time I suggest we brood, talk if we want to, behave like rational sensible human beings and not like a pack of frightened sheep chasing our own shadows."

"Good," he said, "I was hoping you'd say something like that. I couldn't have borne it if you'd devised some party game to take our minds off things."

CHAPTER SEVEN

The window was not locked—but then why bother four floors up and no bedclothes to make a dramatic knotted sheet elopement, no palpitating lover's heart awaiting us below. From the window I could see the entire grounds of the hospital on this side of the building. In the natural perimeter of a hedgerow here and there the gleam of steel mesh wire revealed itself in the trees. At each of the two corners natural buildings had been turned inconspicuously into guard houses, and a set of long low buildings—presumably once stables filled with thoroughbred horses—now appeared to be soldiers' barracks. From this height, the ambulances looked most real—a party of soldiers, however, with typical teutonic thoroughness, was moving one of them nearer to the house—doubtless they knew the R.A.F. constantly took aerial photographs of as much of Europe as possible, and the interpreters' suspicions would be aroused by a number of apparently immobile ambulances. The part of the roof in which these top rooms were located had a sloping mansard and a small six-inch parapet appeared to go all the way along the front. I opened the window wide, and made a sign to the sergeant. He would have preferred to go himself, but now we were all prisoners I felt the severance of that aspect of leadership which insisted I preserve myself for future responsibilities—we were in this together, equal in status, as equal in the ability to take risks as in the power to suffer. I climbed out through the window and lay flat against the lower slope of the mansard, feet jammed in the gutter of the parapet. Provided I lay back flat, there was little danger that anyone on the ground near the house could see me. I worked my way slowly along the roof to the next window, crouched down, and crawled beneath it without risking a look inside. I went along this way to the corner with no interest in the inside of the building—I wanted to make a complete survey of the grounds about us. There would be no difficulty getting to ground level—gutterpipes ran all the way and I'd been up and down enough gutterpipes in the girls hostel at the University to know they were easy to climb. The other side of the building abutted formal gardens, laid out in what I believe is called the Italian fashion, with long walks of evergreen hedges and shaped flower beds between them. The flower beds had been left to seed themselves with weeds, and were now overgrown; the box hedges, too, were in need of a trim and stood three feet high. Once again I traversed the roof, and looked down from the corner over the other side of the building. There were buildings all round a central courtyard on this side, and signs of great activity. This was obviously the main men's barrack block and probably, also, one of the principal entrances to the building for office workers. On the fourth side a stretch of paving carried a number of outdoor chairs, and the ground sloped to a lake. An orderly was already laying a table; presumably the officers' quarters gave on to this terrace. I completed my circular tour, and at last came to the window of the room in which we had been locked, and climbed in. The sergeant indicated everything was all right —no-one had been into the room. I suddenly realised how hungry I was; the sight of the table being laid on the balcony must have stimulated gastric juices—certainly it evoked the many days I had been up early, and walked round a property such as this in its heyday, to come in at breakfast time to a table already laid, kidneys, bacon, eggs and fruit on the sideboard under hot silver dishes. I waved the sergeant close and whispered in his ear.

"We're facing south; the only possible way is west where there's a neglected garden. Down a gutterpipe six feet from the corner with a nasty swing out over the parapet. The gutter is well secured, made of lead, quite strong unless you pull outwards. Socket and wall pins every six feet or so all the way down. To the north the main barracks, the officers mess on the east."

"So they get the early morning sun!"

"So will you if you try going down that way."

I gave the same message to Simon, while the sergeant talked in a loud voice to Jonfey. When I'd finished, the sergeant and Simon talked together and I briefed Jonfey. His eyes lit up when I told him about the gutter—Jonfey could already imagine himself down on the ground and away into the box hedges, crawling fast as a snake.

There were footsteps along the corridor. The key turned in the lock, and a guard came in. He flung the door wide open and somewhat carelessly ushered us out. I could see Jonfey was going to have a go at him and certainly would have killed the man, but I laid a restraining hand on his arm. There was no point in going off half cock, and it was certain that even though we could free ourselves of this much supervision, we wouldn't get out of the house or the grounds without concealing darkness. The German knew that, too; it wasn't apparent in his demeanour he didn't believe we'd be stupid enough to try anything. He led us down two flights of stairs to a long room on the first floor that had been designed as a ballroom, so elegant its furnishings and inlaid wood mosaic floor; the floor was scratched beyond repair. There can have been no third floor above this part of the house, a musicians' gallery curve into the room at one end at a height of about ten feet. Long trestle tables had been laid in the room now used for eating. I was going to say dining, but in view of the litter on the table tops and the mess on the floor, 'fressen' would have been a more appropriate German term than 'essen'—foddering I suppose its nearest English equivalent. Whoever said the Germans are clean precise people had never seen them relaxed and off duty when the vast majority became hog like. We were seated at a trestle table—I could see the expression of distaste on Simon's face as he walked to the side table on which was a bowl of water and a cloth and washed our part of the table clean. A soldier/waiter came from the far end of the hall, carrying a bucket of coffee and a pan of meat, cheeses, bread and pickled onions. It was not our usual breakfast, but I was in no mood to complain—it was certainly a thousand per cent better than anything I had expected. While we were eating, the dapper officer who had captured us came into the hall. The guard eating at the table with us sprang to attention, but we stayed where we were. However, I indicated to the sergeant and the men that they should stop eating; this they would have done anyway as a matter of course. The anomaly of it struck me forcibly—here we were being fed for no other reason than to conserve our strength for the interrogation soon to come. Doubtless the officer who would carry it out was sitting on the terrace, idly picking the last remains of his breakfast from his teeth and smoking a cigar before coming to his duty. And we observed, at least superficially, the traditions of a code of conduct completely outmoded by a three-years-old declaration of total war. I would have felt better had he locked us in a cage, and come to see us carrying a plaited whip. At least we could have sharpened our claws on the bars, and spat defiance at him. But how can you defy a man who smiles and gives each one a Players cigarette doubtless taken from the bruised body of a fellow Englishman, shot down on a bombing mission over this very countryside from which so leisurely you are planning to escape. As he put the cigarette beside Simon's plate, Simon looked up at him.

"Thank you," he said, "but I don't smoke!"

"Perhaps one of the others . . . ?"

"You're very kind," Simon said, and handed the cigarette to Jonfey. Quick thinking—of the four of us, the sergeant was the most addicted to tobacco—Jonfey hardly smoked at all. You don't get the habit, in and out of stables all day.

Without further comment the officer marched out of the hall. The soldier sat down and resumed his meal. I had left a portion of the cheese on my plate—I found it very strong and possibly rancid. The soldier looked at me, and scooped it off my plate and ate it with his fingers.

"Wie heisst er denn, der Kapitan?" I asked. There was no reason to hide my knowledge of German.

"Kapitan Ullan."

"Aus Hamburg?" His accent had betrayed him in the truck.

"Ja, Kapitan Ullan, aus Hamburg. Nun, schweigen Sie, bitte!"

I noted the 'bitte'. He had been well briefed.

As soon as we finished eating he took us out of the building on the north side round the square. At the far end a long low building into which he led us was a makeshift block of lavatories with chemical closets. On these were no doors or separators, and I felt my stomach knot. Sitting on one of the cans a large German corporal was reading an old magazine, much dog-eared. The stench in that house was vile, but he appeared not to notice it.

"I will wait outside," I said to the guard, but he was having none of that. Jonfey, Simon and the sergeant shared none of my inhibitions about performing in semi-public, and I was compelled to wait for them. I looked out of the doorway—at least four hundred men were stationed in the extensive barracks constructed at the back of the house. There was a constant traffic of men into the big house, mostly carrying papers. To my right, in a building I couldn't see, appeared to be another administrative centre into which most of the paper carriers scurried like homing wasps.

When we got back into our room on the top floor, the guard locked the door and left us. As soon as he had gone I opened the window and beckoned the sergeant out. "Only go as far as the corner," I whispered to him. "I don't imagine we'll have long and I'd like Simon and Jonfey to look over the ground." It took him about ten minutes to do his reconnaissance, during which time we were on tenterhooks awaiting the return of the guard. Then Simon went, and when he returned after five minutes, Jonfey went.

We needn't have hurried. It became apparent to me by eleven o'clock that they were in no hurry to interrogate us.

We slept for most of that day—there wasn't a lot to talk about, conscious that at any time they might be listening. I felt I ought to talk to them about interrogation, but I knew nothing other than the standard rules of thumb we had been taught collectively at Braintree, Essex. At least we were re-assured by the knowledge that, provided our captors didn't find them, we had the shards of broken glass and the ulti-mate life or death decision in our own hands. We didn't speak about that, of course.

The sergeant woke me about seven o'clock, as I had asked him. The guard came back about half past seven, and we were taken down to supper. It was the same routine, and a similar meal to breakfast, except that we started with a bowl of thick potato soup into which, unfortunately, the cook had tipped too much pepper. Captain Ullan didn't come to the mess hall, but the guard handed us four cigarettes when we had finished eating. This time, they were of a brand called Black Cat—the Captain must have been running short of Players. We returned upstairs at nine o'clock after our visit to the lavatory shed where once again I could not function. I had resolved that when it became necessary I would go out on the roof rather than squat on one of those evil buck-ets. It would be just my luck if it landed on someone's head.

Simon was pacing about, up and down the room, and I could see it bothered the other two. Jonfey had stretched out on the bed, and the sergeant was sitting at the foot. Back and forwards Simon went, from the door to the window, the window to the bed, the bed to the door.

Finally, "Knock it off, Simon," the sergeant said. "Why don't you sit down and get some rest. You may need all your energy later." Simon came and sat down beside me. "You know," he said, "they ought to give us a story we could tell before we leave England—they ought to fill us up with what sound like valuable facts."

"Why?"

"I've been thinking," he said, "that I don't know any-thing. They can question me all night, but what I know could be told to them in four short sharp sentences."

"Then it won't take long, will it?"

"Yes, but that's the trouble—they won't believe me. They'll think I know a lot more and am concealing it. But I don't. I

don't! I've always made it a policy not to know too much
about what's going on. I didn't want to fill my mind with as-
sorted facts anyone could get out of me the minute they put
the thumb-screws on. I've always believed the less you know,
the less you can tell. But what happens when I've said my
four sentences, and they ask me for the rest, and I say I
don't know any more? They'll never believe me; they'll think
I'm trying to be smart."

What could I say? It was obvious that, like the rest of us,
Simon was scared out of his wits. I too was scared, but
somehow I'd managed to get my fear at least under tem-
porary control. Down there I too would break—but didn't
know what to do about it."

"I was just like this at examination times," Simon continued.
"I just used to seize up. In a viva they once asked me how
I'd deal with a fibrous tumour on a cow's head and I said
amputate its head! I must have been crazy! That set me
back a year."

"It's a funny thing about fear," Jonfey said, from the bed.
"I used to get it when I was show jumping. I remember Midnight—that was the name of a horse—at the International
Horse show in Barcelona, in '37. God, he was a big bugger,
as difficult as they come. They'd shipped him over from
Turin, and I had him on a little farm for a few days to try
to settle him down—he never did like sailing and neither did
I in those days. It was as hot as hell that summer, and he
was really fed up by the time the show came. I had him out
in the enclosure, you know, just warming him up, and I
showed him the three-foot jump they had. He went up to it
in a wild canter, and then the bugger stopped still and stood
straight up on his two hind quarters. I dropped the reins of
course, to try to yank his head down again, but he wasn't
having any. Slowly, and quite deliberately, he came over
backwards. He was determined to crush me. Of course, I
nipped off him a bit sharpish, remounted when he'd picked
himself up, and really squeezed the daylights out of him with
my knees. I took him on the bit so tight he couldn't move an
inch either way and every time he went on to lift his head, I
yanked him down again, fast."

I looked at Simon's face. He was always entranced by
Jonfey's stories of horse jumping—I think of all animals
Simon loved horses the most.

"Well, there was an old vaquero in the enclosure—a right
old lad with skin on him like the shell of a walnut, and he
came across, stood in front of Midnight, blew up its nostrils
and talked to it. He blew right up its nostrils I'm telling you.

That horse settled down, and stopped trembling. Then the man looked up at me and said—in Spanish of course because the old geezer couldn't speak a word of English. 'Why are you afraid?' 'If you'd seen those jumps,' I said to him, 'you'd be afraid—whoever set this course was a bloody sadist!' He smiled at me. 'Yes, señor, it is a good thing to be afraid—that shows your mind is working out the possibilities, but you must never let the horse know.' 'How do you mean, let the horse know—I haven't told him a thing!' This old geezer looked up at me and smiled again—like he was Solomon or something—'You've let him know by your smell. He can smell the sweat of fear on you.' Well, to cut a long story short, we had two clear rounds on Midnight, that day!"

"You took a bath and stopped sweating?" Simon asked, entranced.

"No—the old boy'd been eating garlic soup—after he blew into Midnight's nose, it couldn't smell a thing for the rest of the day! Whenever I jump a horse, these days, I always carry cloves of garlic, and rub them in the horse's nose —I could shit myself with fear, and the horse would never know it!"

Simon got up and walked across to the bed. He rubbed Jonfey's head. "You and your stories," he said, his good humour restored—"I think you make them up half the time!" But he'd got the message!

CHAPTER EIGHT

We waited out the longest two hours of my life. Try as I might I just couldn't get the image of fingernails out of my mind, and all my horror thoughts about the interrogation the Germans must have planned for the dark watches of the night centred on the ten extremities of my hands. I once caught my thumb nail on the bolt of a rifle and ripped it back into the cuticle—the pain came back to me as a conscious throbbing in my thumb. My hands began to feel as if they didn't belong to me—I couldn't keep them still. I tried sitting on them until they were numb, but got pins and needles. I put them in my pockets, but they began to sweat. I clasped, unclasped, kneaded, rubbed and stroked them, spread my fingers out flat on the floor, trying desperately to forget them. By eleven o'clock they felt as big and fat as mess-hall sausages.

I was first to go through the window. The guard changed below at ten o'clock and by eleven the light had almost gone and the guards would be relaxed, a quarter of the way through the tour of duty. There was a guard about a hundred yards from the foot of the gutterpipe, and another over in the corner who seemed to be pacing the north side. I debated sending the others down different gutterpipes, but that only increased the number of targets over the area of observation.

"Twenty feet apart. The pipe is not jointed so it won't make any difference to the pressure on the pins if we're all on the pipe together, as long as we don't get two to any one section. And, if you fall, push yourself out from the wall—no-one will want to catch you! Me first, the sergeant, then Simon—Jonfey last. Make your own way through the garden and rendezvous by that small shed at the bottom west corner. Don't try to go through the wire or touch it—it may be plugged in to the mains and though they only use a hundred and twenty volts here, you could set bells ringing."

They all nodded.

"And good luck," I said, as I swung myself sickeningly over the parapet. There's only one way to get on a gutter if the parapet overhangs. You go over the side, hanging by your waist, and feel for it with your feet. You can't see what you're feeling for. The gutterpipe usually has a large cup at the top, and you must be careful not to be deluded into thinking you can grip it—those cups are rarely fastened tight. The first secure foothold was six feet down the gutter. I gripped the side of the pipe with my feet, held one hand on the actual parapet edge, and let my body slide down until I was hanging one-handed with my feet resting against the square corners of the lead pipe. My left hand I pushed beneath the parapet, beneath the water-gathering cone to where the pipe itself was held into the stone. I pulled against the connection—good, it was firm. A grip with that lower left hand and slowly let go with my right. My feet slipped down the pipe about twelve inches, my weight thrown backwards away from the wall. My body slipped downwards in a dreadful lurch that seemed to last for ever, but the rubber cleats of my Innsbrucker boots caught the first pipe connection, a grab forward with my right hand and I was safe. From now on it was child's play. Shift hand grips until fingers are caught in the slight crevice between pipe and wall and bend the knees. Ankles together, lift feet off pins and bobbins that hold the pipe to the wall, and slide down a section keeping backside out and shoulders forward to push the centre of balance as close to the wall as possible. Each section felt like a drop of a hundred and fifty feet, but gradually I slid down each one without incident or noise. It was only when I had gone five sections I gained confidence to pause, look up, and then down. The sergeant was on the second section; no sign of anyone on the ground beneath us other than the sentry I had already spotted, and he was looking at ground level the other way. The face of the wall was comparatively light, or so it seemed to me, but there was no moon as yet. Section seven, then section eight.

If only no-one goes into that fourth-floor room until we are on the ground! We had jammed the door with the wash hand stand to delay entry but we couldn't count on more than minutes. Now for section nine.

The ninth section was loose and came away from the wall as I slid down it. I grabbed upwards with my right arm and caught the bobbin of the section above. One handed, I hung there, my heart bumping, then slowly lifted my shoulders until my head was level with the break. The lead had pulled away from the socket. Both pins were secure. I took a grip with my left hand and slowly pulled myself, hand over hand, up the eighth section until I could lodge my feet on the pins.

The ninth section, I could see, had dropped down about four inches, the four inches that held it to the section above. Keeping my feet on the bobbins, I ran my hand grip down, crouching. The movement pulled me away from the wall of course and if the eighth section were loose, nothing could prevent me falling backwards. I gripped the side of the eighth section with the inner sides of my boots, spread my knees and heels as far apart as possible, and reached down with my left hand, between my knees. I could feel the strain pulling at my sacroiliac joint at the base of the spine. My face was jammed tight against the pipe—gritty against my sweaty cheek and jaw. I kept sliding my right hand grip slowly down, left hand reaching down between my feet, until I could grasp the ninth section. It was too fat for me to span it with my hand, but gradually I got my thumb on the front of it and the tips of two fingers around it, and tried to lift. If only I could lift it three inches I had hopes of jamming it around the eighth section protruding below the collar. I looked up. The sergeant was two sections above me, looking anxiously down. He daren't come any lower to help me. I looked down. There were another six sections to go after the ninth—a drop of forty feet. One of us was sure to hurt an ankle. I'd have risked it alone—but the law of averages was against taking the same risk four times.

I couldn't lift the lead pipe. It was too heavy, and I was in too awkward a position to use my strength effectively. I looked up again at the sergeant and indicated he should descend to where I was. He started to move, but I stopped him, indicating that I would go down first then come back up. He understood. I hung hands only from the bobbins. I let my feet hang as far down as possible, below the next set of bobbins. The broken pipe was between my knees, useful only as a guide. I managed to jam the sides of my boots tight against it, said a quick prayer, and dropped free. My feet caught the next bobbins first, my body started to go backwards since I couldn't hold on to the broken pipe with my hands, and then my hands caught the next bobbins and held. I looked up. The sweat that had gathered on my forehead ran into my eyes; I tried wiping it away with a cuff but it was heavily salted, no doubt from fear. My bladder had also leaked.

The sergeant climbed quickly down the pipe until he was standing where I had stood, and he too squatted. He took a grip on the pipe from above, I took one from below, and we pushed the section back into place. A wooden wedge, used for jamming the pipes, had moved. I hammered it back into position using the flat of my hand—the sergeant used his Innsbruckers as best he could to bend the flange of the pipe back over the section above. He reached down and tested the section. It held. The guard had heard nothing.

I gained the ground without further troubles. The sergeant waited two sections below until Simon had crossed the ninth, then Simon waited until Jonfey had crossed it. As soon as Jonfey was on the last sections I ran, half squatting, into the protection of the three feet high box hedges of the formal garden. Looking back at the house there were no signs of disturbance. I made my way easily through the hedges and arrived at the shed in the far corner of the garden. No-one was near it. The shed was surrounded entirely by garden debris—two compost heaps behind it, and the remains of stakes and sticks and boxes, a few rusty spades with long handles in the Dutch fashion. Already the wood had rotted, the metal rusted. Jonfey arrived first, then Simon and, after an agonising five minutes, the sergeant appeared, carrying a pair of wire cutters, new looking and well greased.

"There was a tool shed behind that shit house—I saw it this morning. Keep your eyes open, lads," he said.

I knew the reproof was also meant for me—but sergeants are born, not made. I went round the back of the shed, leaving Jonfey and Simon on watch, and crawled towards the wire. It had been laced through a screen of Cupressus Macrocarpus and couldn't, therefore, have been electrified—every movement of a bough would have set the bells ringing. But there was a nasty little trip wire about eighteen inches this side of it, and looking through the mesh I could see the same arrangement on the other side, and those two trip wires were electrified and hanging from porcelain connectors. The wire itself, however, was not taut. "It's got to touch the earth," the sergeant said, "before it sends a signal." I stepped over it and started to work on the wire mesh with the clippers the sergeant had acquired. Within two minutes I had clipped a hole four feet wide and a couple of feet high, taking care to keep the cut section in one piece. Then we both bent it upwards, away from the trip wire. I went through, then the sergeant gave a long low breathy whistle without a musical note for Simon and Jonfey. After the the sergeant slid through, we bent back the wire and twisted it into position. Except from close up, it would be difficult to see the mesh had been disturbed.

We ran.

We had travelled the best part of a mile when we heard the dull clamour of the alarm. Until that moment we had been running anywhere. Their knowledge of our escape, however, gave us a sense of direction—we were trying to get home.

"What did you say," I asked the sergeant, "it's a long way home and I hope we don't have to walk it or swim!"

The moon had come out and we headed west—at least we wouldn't have to circle the camp to get on our correct bearing. As to where we were, and what we were going to do, I had to confess myself without a single idea. I halted the men in the lee of a hedge on the other side of a road that ran north and south. They gathered about me in a tight circle.

"I've no need to tell you our present dilemma," I said. "We're in enemy territory, lost, without weapons or food."

"We can find an enemy camp and raid it!" Jonfey said. I think he had no realisation of the seriousness of our position —either that, or was determined not to admit to it, since that could be the first symptoms in an epidemic of contagious fear, hysteria and ultimate surrender. I'd spent too many nights alone in deep country to be afraid of hobgoblins. But at the present moment I was charged with the responsibility of three men without food or weapons and every bush like Burnham woods could suddenly shout death at us. We had been taken once and had escaped—this time they would make certain escape was physically impossible.

"Do we stay together," Simon asked, "or separate?" Bless him, he was trying to let me off the hook, was saying, 'Do you want to try to make it alone, unburdened by us three.' He thought we all stood a better chance separated—though I couldn't disagree with him, a fierce pride rose in me. These were my men. I trained them to the point of readiness for this assignment; I gave the order that brought them here. I brought them, and I was going to take them back whole and safe in one unit if that were possible. You take on the responsibility of other men's lives without thinking of your own safety. Of course it might have been easier to get home without them, but I couldn't be certain they would get home unless I were there to help them. That of course was a terrible arrogance; a feeling anything they would be asked to do, I would be able to do for them, better than they could do it themselves. Who knows, perhaps by my very presence I impeded their progress down avenues of thought and spontaneous action that would lead them safely home. But I did, sincerely, think more of us would get back home together quickly and safely if we stayed as a party, and I led that party.

Also I knew that only in that way could I expunge the

guilt I felt for the mistake at the tree—the mistake for which constantly I blamed myself.

The only one to argue would be Jonfey. The sergeant would accept what I said without thinking, and Simon could be swayed by argument. But Jonfey had about him a dash and verve I couldn't rationally match—the young colt who wants to jump all hedges, to charge because inactivity is wasteful of the natural energy with which he was abundantly endowed. As long as Jonfey thought we had a plan in mind and were prepared to execute it, he would go along with whatever was suggested and did. He was like the air that must rush in whenever it suspects a vacuum, mercury that rises and falls with each change of temperature and pressure.

"This house must have been on the western edge of Meldenkirche," I said, "since the lorries didn't go through the town when they were taking us there, and didn't travel far enough to get round it to the north or south. If we continue to head west we should come to the railway. If we can get there, we shall be able to find the wreck of that train, and if we find that, we can find our former position." Three 'ifs' in a row. There had been three radios, protected from damage by falling—they had to be since we jumped with them on our backs. The radios had been thrown out of the tree —doubtless a few connections were broken, but if we could repair them . . . it was the biggest if, but I was determined to try it.

"I think we stay together," I said to Simon, "but I'm prepared to take a vote on it."

The sergeant shook his head. Jonfey shook his head. No vote—we'd stay together. I took the lead again, and headed due west, reading our direction by the stars, and keeping the Plough and the North Star to my right. Whenever we came to a road, we watched it carefully for several minutes before crossing it. Twice we were nearly caught by motorcycle combinations, but managed to evade them. Once an armoured column moved northwards, once we had to wait until an infantry company came marching up the road, in single file, one rank at each side of the road. It took them twenty minutes to pass—Jonfey as ever wanted to knock off a couple of their rifles and field rations, but I would have none of it. I was quite confident we could have taken at least three of the stragglers, but the risk, however small, was too great to take. The Germans would certainly be looking for us heading west, but they could not be certain we had not gone south or north to deceive them and would deploy some of their available effort and manpower in those

directions. I certainly didn't want to put a mark on the map
for them to use as a search centre—the column was bound
to halt in forty-five minutes or so, and lost stragglers would
be noted.

A farm cart had been left in a corner of a field. The sergeant looked in the box beneath the seat. In the box were
ten apples. We ate the lot. The juice was wonderful. In a
field about a mile further on we came across potatoes grow-
ing and dug them with our fingers. They tasted bitter until
we rubbed the skins off—again, the juice was a blessing.
That peppery soup must also have been salty, with the pepper hiding the salt taste—or perhaps the knowledge we
were short of food and water made us symptomatically more
hungry and thirsty. I stuffed five potatoes in my battle-dress
blouse—they would make useful gut filler when we needed
them. We had crossed the railway and were almost within
sight of the tree when we had our first real stroke of luck.
A Mercedes car had stopped by the side of the road, and the
driver and his guard passenger, a corporal, were squatting
down in the hedge, relieving themselves. Jonfey's idea of
course was to take them immediately and drive the car to
the coast but, cautious as ever, the sergeant and I crawled
as near as we dared and listened to them. It soon became
apparent they were lost, their destination at least ten miles
to the west on the other side of the Maas. They had come
from about thirty miles to the east, and were not expected
to reach their destination until midday the following day.
They had been delayed by a couple of girls! It was an opportunity too good to miss. I wish it could have been otherwise, but we could afford to take no risks. Kill or be killed.
I got one with a rabbit chop that broke his neck. The sergeant strangled the other. Jonfey and Simon put on their
battle dress tops and caps, and the sergeant and I sat in the
back of the Mercedes, low down, ready to drop to the floor
if we should run into a patrol. The corporal had a rifle and
nearly a hundred rounds of ammunition—not automatic but
at least it was a weapon; the driver had a pistol and ten
rounds—a nine-millimetre Luger, fast and accurate.

The boot of the car was literally full of food and drink.
On the back seat were a map case, an envelope containing
the particulars of the vehicle and its permission to move, and
the movement orders for the driver, Hans Kellerman, and
the corporal, Martin Brueckner. There was also a pair of
girls' knickers—the elastic had been broken on one leg and
at the waist. No doubt one of the two had scratches on his
face—but we didn't stop to look. We carried them a distance

from the road and dumped them in the bed of a boggy
stream, covered with branches, where dogs would not scent
them.

We drove the car in the direction of the tree, to the spot
where the lorries and the scanner van had been parked, then
the sergeant and I went to look for the radios.

"You'd better get out and pretend to be doing what the
other two were doing," I said. "But make certain you both
face opposite directions."

Simon opened the nearside door. "I wish we hadn't killed
them," he said. "At least not then. We could have waited—
it seems a rotten moment to die. There's a disease that monkeys get—it blocks up the anus eventually, and the monkeys
strain to get it out, and can't, and usually burst a blood vessel,
trying too hard. I've always thought it a rotten moment to
die—even for monkeys."

CHAPTER NINE

Two of the three sets were still in working order. The power packs had suffered but we were able to jump a wire across two of them to give us enough juice for a transmission.

We got Rugby first call, and they gave us Braintree.

"Where the hell have you been?" he asked.

"Change to the frequency of the number above your office door," I said, and switched off. I gave him time to get through to Rugby, and then started to look for him on the forty-metre waveband. I got him within a minute, tuned in my BFO, and netted on to him. Then I called and he got me first time. The Braintree line was open.

"Can you send a plane—same when and where?" Then I switched off transmission. They weren't catching me again —it takes at least a minute to tune a direction finder, even if you know the frequency, and are listening when the transmission starts.

He came back on the air in three minutes. By God he was quick, and both the Army and the Air Force duty officers must have been at their desks for a change—or perhaps he was acting on his own initiative. "Slight problem. Increased ack-ack left of flight path, or so we hear. You'd never get through. Two batteries."

"Where?"

"Four plus three from previous datum."

That meant four miles north and three miles south of the hayrick. We could find them. I turned to the sergeant. "Can we knock out two ack-ack batteries?" I asked him. He nodded, instantly.

"Leave them to us and send in this plane."

"Marvellous if you manage, old man," he said, his voice coming and going on the longer wave of the forty-metre band—"they're messing up a party we'd planned for somewhere else."

"Give us four hours—so still same where and when, over and out."

We hadn't been on 'transmit' for longer than seven seconds at any one time—no-one could have tracked us.

65

Nevertheless we fled from that tree like bats out of the caves of hell, and thanks to the Mercedes were within a half mile of the first ack-ack battery within thirty-five minutes. We had passed plenty of vehicles and troops on the road, but there was safety in numbers apparently, and no-one stopped or showed the slightest sign of interest in us. The bandages the sergeant and I wrapped round our heads possibly helped—we were able to loll back on the seats in style and comfort, and earned sympathetic glances from everyone we passed. The GHQ insignia, fore and aft, probably helped as much as the bandages. Jonfey drove the car well, despite the lack of illumination—the headlamps had been covered with black paper leaving only a small cross free to transmit the light. Several times we were saved from the ditch only by Simon's keen lookout, but I was in no mood to tell Jonfey to slow down, and he had not the temperament to dawdle.

For the first time since we left the house, we were able to converse. This account of our escape will inevitably be short of dialogue because we were seldom able to talk to each other in voices louder than whispers—and somehow that constraint also cuts down the amount you say. For the first time we were able to let ourselves go in the heart's-easing kind of banality that opens the stop-cock on relief of tension.

"I thought you were a goner, sir, when that pipe pulled off the wall." "So did I, I can tell you." "My God, didn't that lead feel gritty." "Give me an iron pipe, any day." "I could do with a smoke—that's the one thing I miss, not being able to light a fag whenever you want to." "I wonder how Lieutenant Masters is getting on, sir?" "I'll bet he's had Robert on a couple of fizzers"—a quick need to reassert discipline—"The Lieutenant is a good officer—the trouble is that some of you don't give him a chance—you'll see, he'll be a first-class officer in action." "Will we get leave when we get back?" "Sevenpence a day danger money for this little lot, you know!"

We came to the first ack-ack site on the other side of a wood at the edge of the road. We skirted it, and then drove down the road looking for the other. It was a half mile away in open country. Not so good! Simon and I would take the open field—Jonfey and the sergeant the wood.

"What shall we try?" the sergeant asked. "Sights, or ammo?"

"Both, one on each."

We made our arrangements about a rendezvous, and they dropped us off a quarter mile from the second ack-ack unit.

An ack-ack unit is a self-contained military organism,

based on a number of guns and the men to fire them. With
the guns you have transport to shift the guns and the men.
With the transport you have tents for the men to live in, and
cookhouses to feed the men who live in the tents and shoot
the guns. Officers command the men, and if they're lucky
they get a caravan, with plotting tables, maps and charts,
an easy chair, a bunk bed, a radio and as many creature
comforts as they can cram into a space eight feet by six. A
signals section takes the orders to fire or not to fire, and an
ammunition section brings up the shells. An ack-ack carries
shells with it, unlike fixed artillery units that don't use so
many and can have them in planned dumps some distance
from the gun site. One of our standard lessons—this time
in Scotland, not Wales, had been 'how to do sites, gun, ack-
ack, German'! 'Do' was the most overworked word in a
soldier's vocabulary.

You can knock out the radio unit—but that can always
be replaced by other radio units or land-line telephone units.
Secondly you can spike the guns, but for that you need explosives to slip inside the barrel—the explosive makes the barrel
look like a squashed cigar if you blow it correctly. The third
text-book method is to spoil the ammunition—this you can
do either by tampering with the fuses, or by setting the ammo
dump on fire. A fourth and unofficial method is to take a
nail file or a bent nail or, luxury even, a screwdriver and
alter the setting of the sights.

The men of the ack-ack unit were all on stand down.
Four guards; one behind the cookhouse tent drinking coffee;
one guarding the officer's caravan—it was actually a converted horsebox from the look of it; one sitting on the pile
of ammunition, and one dozing in the front seat of a half
track used for pulling guns out of mud. Seven guns were
laid in arrowhead formation of three, two, one, one. Behind
each gun a small stack of ammunition, ready for loading.
I was about two hundred yards from the cookhouse tent,
directly in line with the front gun, open field to cross, with
short grass. Simon went round the other side, his immediate target the gun in the centre of the three on the back rank.
He had a screwdriver from the tool kit in the car; I had the
flat sharp end of a file that would do the same job. It was a
long way across that field, belly-crawling all the way. It's
one thing to crawl across a Welsh mountainside with one of
your own boys aiming tracer as near to you as he dare; the
risks are there, but somehow, you never believe he will hit
you. With four men on guard, the nearest not two hundred
yards away with a Schmeizer, it was hard to believe they

could miss you. Crawling is a matter for wide legs, the inside of the foot and knees pressed to the ground. But it's also a matter of pressing your belly so hard to the ground you scrape your skin against the inside of your clothing, scared lest your arse lift even an inch in the air. You're not worried about getting one in the head—that stays well down; or your back which is sucked flat against your ribs; it's your arse, and the base of the spine at the coccyx you fear for. Even a hundred yards of crawling under the open muzzle of a gun gives you a pain in the coccyx. I had two hundred yards to go!

Once in the shelter of the gun I was able to lift myself from the ground behind the pile of ammunition. Ack-ack guns use a special shell, primed to explode in the air at a given height, plastering the skies with fragments. Ack-ack gunners are not concerned with trying to hit the airplane, the shell itself could go through the plane without doing much damage. But a thousand flying fragments can tear hell out of the mechanism of a plane. The height at which the shell will explode is set immediately before the shell is fired, on the orders of the gunnery officer. The setting is very simple—a brass ring round the base is turned to a specific number engraved on the shell's perimeter. The ring is secured to the base of the shell by a number of screws, depending which make it is. These shells had three. It took only a second to locate the three screw heads. My file end fitted exactly. Without moving the top shell from the pile I unfastened the three screw heads and gently eased the back off, pulling it towards me. If I were to drop it, the pile of shells and me with it would go sky high. Inside the shell casing a wheel was fastened to a spindle by two screws. I unfastened those two screws and turned the spindle to its limit, clockwise. I left the screws untightened and pulled the spring away from the clock mechanism in the shell casing before putting the back on.

The shell itself would not explode in the breach of the gun the second it was fired. The distance would be called out by the gunnery officer, the gunner's armourer would turn the setting on the shell case (though this would have no effect since I had disconnected the spindle and spring), the gunner's mate would load the shell into the breach, the gunner take elevation and direction from the gunnery officer, set his gun on target allowing for wind velocity, height parabola and all the other calculable factors; the gunner's mate, tense, would watch all this and dream of his promotion to gunner; at the nod of the gunner's head, the mate would take his moment of glory and yank the lanyard. The firing mechanism in the breech of the gun would snap forwards striking the detonator that explodes the small charge needed to get the shell spinning skywards; but now there was no time delay between that explosion and the next, no delayed action as the shell winged its way towards a skyborne target. The second that detonator exploded the small firing charge, the main fragmentation charge would explode, thousands of cubic feet of hot air would try to escape from the end of the thin barrel, and fail, and the breech of the gun would be puffed out and shattered like Chinese finger crackers, whamming the fragments of metal in all directions. With seven explosive centres, few people on the gunsight could survive.

It took two and a quarter hours to 'do' all the shells on the top of the piles. I met Simon midway through the job. He was altering the zero setting of the range-finders; the guns would aim low and to the left in case, for any reason, they didn't use the shells I had so carefully prepared for them. "I wouldn't care to be within half a mile when they fire this lot," he said grinning. 'Neither would I!'

I was still working on the shell from the last pile, the rear gun to the left of the back of the pyramid, when suddenly the alert sounded. I hadn't heard the drone of any plane. Within seconds, flaps on tents opened as men rushed out in stages of undress. A small hollow in the field ran off to one side, I ran crouched over to it and dropped in. Hardly was I down before flying feet passed above my head as the first gunner leaped over. He was followed by five others. I dared not move lest a late-comer should see me, then, fear bending my back low, I shuffled along the bottom of that depression until about twenty yards from the line between the tents and the guns. I hoped Simon had managed to hide himself somewhere—his task harder since he would be exposed at the front of the guns where, if I remembered correctly, was only open field and a dyke, with water stretching away beyond.

The gunners were intent on only one direction, forward and upward. There had been a brief spilling of light as the master gunner came from the officer's horsebox caravan—he was wearing headphones and doubtless was connected by line or short-distance radio to the officer himself, receiving his instructions by radio from the meteorological and tracking-station personnel.

Despite the risk of being seen, I bent myself double, and ran dodging from side to side to make myself less of a target.

I had only travelled a hundred yards or so before there was a sudden shout and the rifle fire began. Shots screamed past me as I ran, wildly zigzagging backwards and forwards, bent double. It's difficult to hit a running man with a rifle bullet, even if you are a crack shot, which not many soldiers are—but with bullets whistling past me at a distance of not much more than twelve inches, that knowledge was small comfort to me. Then, despite the sounds of the Schmeizer fire, and the crack of the bullets zipping past me and the thump as they hit the trees ahead, I heard the planes. I flung myself to the ground and waited. The master gunner was calling out elevation, range, fuse settings. The rifle shots were getting closer to me, some whistling not inches from my head. Tortuously I twisted so the right side of my body was the one exposed to them—it was an irrational thing to do since the target was increased across the arc of fire.

The master gunner called his final command—I could imagine the snap as the gunner's mate pulled hard at the lanyard in correct Teutonic orderly style, and there was an almighty thump as the shells were detonated to start them on their screaming journey through the air. There was the instant sound of a whistle on a low note, more a sort of bass moan, and then it was as if the crust of hellfire had been uncapped and the spurting pressure from within suddenly released. The sound of it was an almost simultaneous series of claps of thunder, with the crack of lightning thrown in for good measure as fragments of the guns were scattered at random, and then the shells themselves on the ground began to explode, a rhythmic series of giant thuds that made the surface of the field tremble like a giant jelly. I was tossed up into the air by the vibration, then swatted like a fly some twenty yards or so into the shrubberies ahead of me. The trees themselves had been bent by the blast before I got there, and snapped back. One of them, an eight-inch diameter sapling, whipped back like a bamboo stake and hit me in the stomach. I felt a rib crack before the air was expelled from my body and I fell. My last conscious moment as I hit the ground, rolling, was of a flaming ball rolling along the ground where the ack-ack site had been, and a plume of thick black oily smoke starting to rise. I don't know for how long I was unconscious—when I came to the black cloud had settled and it was apparent our scheme had succeeded beyond anything we could have hoped. There must have been some new kind of explosive in those shells, explosive with some inflammatory potential since the entire edifice of the ack-ack unit, such as it was, tents, horsebox, canvas topped vehicles, had been set alight. The wood itself, into which I had been flung, bore the heavy stench of burning new growth. I must have been unconscious but still capable of movement since I recovered consciousness almost at the far side of the wood—possibly, like a headless chicken, I had run the last fifty yards with the electric ends of my nerves activating muscles.

I made my way to the rendezvous, uncertain what to expect. There was utter confusion on the roads, since the neighbouring units thought the ack-ack unit had been destroyed by aerial bombardment. Several times I stood silent in the hedge and heard shouted warnings of bombardment as men jog-trotted past, moving out of the imagined danger.

Simon was waiting at the rendezvous—wet through, but completely unhurt. As soon as the alert sounded, he had dived over the dyke into the canal. The suction and concussive effect of the explosion had almost emptied the canal at that point, had scooped him out of the water over the dyke again.

Jonfey and the sergeant killed a man to get to their guns. Their unit had exploded less than a minute after ours—but they had completed the job faster and were already back in the wood when the units exploded. Though my breathing was still erratic I had not cracked a rib, Simon said, but would have a helluva bruise there within an hour.

Jonfey's face was beaming like a happy schoolboy. "Well done," was all he could say, "bloody well done."

By dawn's first light we were waiting on the landing strip, cold and hungry, but for my part no longer constipated.

CHAPTER TEN

The plane came in to land exactly on time. One minute nowhere, next it was skimming over the hedge top in a once only landing run. The long field was absolutely flat, an ideal landing strip. I couldn't think why the Germans had not mined it, or ridged it—another of those strange gaps in efficiency I frequently noted throughout the war—the Achilles' heel of totalitarianism. Take away a man's initiative and he will be responsible for nothing, creative about nothing— give a man his head and every single act becomes a challenge. The plane must have flown in so low it missed the ack-ack screen and the spotters, since no-one opened fire on it. I knew we could not be so lucky getting out. The minute we rose over the skyline they'd throw flaming steel confetti at us from all sides. The plane's wheels touched the ground at the far end of the field and he started to taxi—he was travelling fast, but the field was long enough to take him at any speed. He had a large tree as a running line, and we waited at his approximate stopping point in the field, ready to manhandle him around for his take-off. He landed downwind, would take off into the wind to lift his nose over the hedge.

He had run about two hundred yards ground speed down to about a hundred and ten, I would judge, when his brakes locked on, hard. I heard the rasp of the tortured brake drums, and the plane tipped straight up forwards, and the whirring propellor crashed into the ground. The plane turned completely over. There was a sickening smack as it broke its back and the tail plane fell loose in front of it. I was already about fifty yards towards it, the sergeant running fast behind me. Jonfey and Simon I waved back. There had been enough petrol in that plane to get us home. When we got there, the pilot was dead, his back, like that of the plane, snapped. It was the pilot who had brought us in. We dragged him clear of the wreckage. Simon and Jonfey came over to where we put him on the grass. Simon looked at him, but we didn't need Simon to tell us he was dead.

"He's dead," Simon said, "let's get going."

I shook my head, dully. This man had brought us in,

risked his life to be the one to bring us out. Each of these flying missions is a voluntary assignment. How can you just walk away from a man like that?

"Pavlov's dogs," Simon said, quietly. Only I heard it. Like a puppet I turned on my heel. "Come on," I said, "Let's get out of here." I took the lead, heading across the field in a jog-trot. It couldn't take many minutes for the Germans to find the field and the plane.

"Oh dear God," I remember thinking as I jogged along. "Just once, let's go back, for however short a time, to being human beings. Just for one short time, let's obliterate the war, let's bury a man we've killed, let's not kill a man, let's go back, for just one short second, to a human existence." I knew it was a vain hope. Like Pavlov's dogs we were conditioned, like Pavlov's dogs we would stay. But that man dressed himself, walked across the tarmac and climbed into his plane. He had no need to do it. He could have stayed at home, he could have gone off duty. For him the war, momentarily, could have ended with a glass of beer and a pipe of tobacco. But it didn't. He volunteered again, to fly to fetch us out. And we said thank you by running away from him.

CHAPTER ELEVEN

When we arrived back at the car, a German patrol had found it. We had kept the rotor arm—but it was a useless gesture. So many soldiers were milling about that area we dared not go near the tree. I couldn't see us getting into contact again with Rugby, the broken batteries had barely sustained our last transmission. For a while that radio set had given me the comfort of a house full of telephones with guidance at the other end of a continuous wire; now we were isolated, cut off from the source of wisdom.

We set off to walk slowly to the west, to the sea, to home. I felt like Charlie Chaplin at the end of a film.

We had two alternatives. We were between Wallwijk and 's-Hertogenbosch, in territory mostly grassland—the tree belt of pines, oaks and beeches started ten miles in front of us to the west, and then we had another twenty-five miles or so to travel to the flat lands, the polders at the delta of the Maas. Once in the polders, I was confident we could lose ourselves along the extensive waterways, making our way slowly out towards and past Willemstad, Ooltgensplaat, and into Zeeland. Somewhere along the way we'd look for a fishing boat, since they were still operating in coastal waters, under German Naval supervision of course, to sneak us over the North Sea to England. We should be able to find something in Haamstede, or Ouddorp, or Zieriksee.

The alternative was to strike south, into Belgium. After all we were only about twenty miles north of the Belgian-Dutch Border at its nearest point, and I knew several people in Antwerp and further south in Brussels—less than a hundred miles away. On balance I favoured the open polders of Zeeland—and there was a distinct psychological advantage anyway in travelling west, away from the Germans and Germany, towards the North Sea however wide it may seem and however distant England on its far shores.

How do you travel through open country during the day? If there's a road going your way you take a chance. You put one man in front, leave one man behind, and travel as a team, constantly looking backwards and forward to keep in touch with your scouts. You can never shout at each other, of course, so you depend on always staying in vision of each other. It's tiring business. Nor can you ever travel in the comfortable centre of the road too far from the hedgerows. It's not as difficult as it sounds. Mostly, in open countryside, you can see for long distances before you can be seen. You are vitally interested in anyone who may be about—usually they are not interested in you unless you give them reason, and surprisingly, soldiers in occupied territory do not keep a constant alert. We travelled all morning, and at midday discovered a small wood and crawled in there to sleep. We were all exhausted, and Jonfey's side was aching again. He needed two or three days of inactivity, sitting on a deck-chair on a sun-drenched beach—he should have his dressing changed twice a day. Above all, he needed the one thing we couldn't give him, the opportunity to stay still for a time. His wound was not infected—merely throbbing in anger at not being left to knit in peace.

We dragged wearily off the road, into the wood, waiting until Simon, our rear scout, came level with us before penetrating deeply into the trees. It was a clean wood with little undergrowth near the side of the road. Only further back were there bushes and shrubs we could get down into to make our simple bivouacs. At the far end of the wood was a flowing stream of clear water—one by one as best we could we washed ourselves in it and drank. I took off my rubber-soled Innsbrucker boots and bathed my feet—they are ideal for climbing and walking over rough country, but on gritty roads they pick up small stones between the cleats and become hot and uncomfortable.

"If only we could make a fire and cook some grub!" Jonfey said. His was the voice of all of us. Looking round I could see the lines of strain beginning to show on faces—and knew they must be etched into mine. Without the opportunity to shave, we looked a band of brigands. Some people grow hair on their faces in a dignified fashion, an overall bristle that soon is acceptable as a beard. The sergeant and Simon were both of that type, dark and swarthy by nature, it wasn't long before the hirsute growths looked deliberate. Jonfey, however, grew his hair in untidy wisps —as I felt I did. I had an itching growth under my chin, nothing on the flat sides of my cheek at all—long growths at the extremities of my upper lip and very little in the centre. Jonfey saw me rubbing my chin.

"You don't feel you've had a proper wash if you can't shave with it, do you?" I agreed with him. He sat down in the bivouac area, his boots and socks in his hand 'letting my dogs get some air', he said. He looked at his feet. "Still," he said, "it's better than walking in riding boots, and many's the time I've had to walk home when a horse has bolted with me and thrown me. It's strange the way a horse will take you miles and once he's got rid of you, will turn round and trot quietly back to the stable."

"That's life," the sergeant said. "Takes you to the end of your tether and drops you."

"Hark at the philosopher," Jonfey quipped, but without malice. It was good they still had the interest to talk in this way—you can tell when men are fatigued mentally as well as physically by the silences—I didn't mind tired bodies, but there'd come a time soon we'd need minds as alert as whippets. And as fast.

"What do you think is our chance of getting in touch with the Underground?" the sergeant asked. "What do they call themselves, the Stooetroopen?"

"I don't think there's much chance around here—I think they're mostly active further east, and down at Maastricht —there are units in the towns—Rotterdam and Amsterdam —but I don't think we should go near them. All I want is a leisurely walk through this flat land—as far as the water. Then we can pick up a fishing boat, and get away at night down one of the lesser-used estuaries. I don't anticipate much difficulty, as long as we keep alert and use our heads when the time comes."

"That's the problem," Simon said—"walking along like this induces a state of euphoria—your mind slips back and forwards—somehow it won't stay in the present. For the last mile along the road I was planning a walk I would like to do sometime down the Caledonian canal from Inverness, and wondering whether it would be worth taking a small canoe to try to make it through the lochs."

"That's what they call escapism," Jonfey said, "and that's something we need a lot of, right now!" We all groaned at the deliberate pun.

"It's a dangerous business, Simon, and I'd warn you against it. If you're not careful you'll be half way down the Caledonian canal in your mind and your body will be knocked down by a squadron of tanks."

"How do you do it, then? How do you keep your mind on the present, walking along the ditch like that?"

"Two things. One I always count the steps, always. Up to a thousand, then start again. That gives me a conscious scheme of the distance we travel. I used to do that as a boy, in the Dales. How many steps from the top of one dale to the next, and then pace it to see how right I was. The other is that I mark the spots in my mind from which I think an attack might come—the obvious ones, and then I try to find all the non-obvious ones, and count an extra point for every one I can find. I divide the countryside up into stretches, and if I can count ten for each stretch I think I'm doing well. What do you do, sergeant?"

"I look at the countryside in arcs. I start, shall we say left of arc, and slowly I look from left of arc to right of arc along a fixed distance. Then I sweep left again to the extreme left of arc, moving up all the time."

"But what happens," Simon asked, "if someone or something should appear right of arc when you're busy looking left of arc?"

"The sudden movement, you see, gives them away. I look for movement, all the time, even little things like birds flying, rabbits, little things like that."

"How about you, Jonfey?" I asked.

"Oh, it's easy with me," he said. "I always look at a piece of ground as if I was hunting over it, as if I'd got a horse clapped between my knees. You can't afford to miss much when you're out hunting. There's many a squire been killed because he put a high-spirited horse into a jump at a hedge and a pheasant flew out under the horse's nose. A horse won't jump a hedge if there's anything in it. You learn to spot it— loose fence rails, pheasants, chickens near a farm—even feathers a fox has left, fluttering in the hedgerows."

"That's all right," Simon said, "that's what you look for, but what do you think about?"

"Birds," he said, "the human variety. Birds in jodhpurs, birds out of jodhpurs—birds in britches, birds out of britches. Oh yes, you can go a long way in a short time, thinking about birds!" We all laughed, the tension relieved. I didn't believe him for a moment, but there could be no future analysing methods. Our training was over, and our methods were already in-built, if we had any at all. And if we had none, then God help us.

"Make out a guard roster, sergeant," I said, "and include me—I don't mind going first, if no-one else cares to."

We passed the rest of the day, holed up in that wood, usually two sleeping and one on guard, one off duty if there can be such a thing. Heavy infantry and motorised units moved along the main road—several times I ventured through the trees to watch them. Most of the columns headed north, towards Amsterdam and Rotterdam, and I guessed the

High Command was reinforcing its Dutch Occupation force. It was one of those idyllic days in early June when the sun is warm but not too hot, the sky clear but not cloudless, the air comparatively still, but with occasional freshening winds. Inside the wood was cool, the light filtered by the overgrowth. There was a moment's anxiety about five o'clock when one of the units, foot-borne infantry, pulled in off the road to rest and prepare food. They were there for nearly an hour before a senior officer in a staff car came along the road and got them moving again. The smell of the food was agonising—but they didn't leave a scrap. We looked.

This was a thickly populated area, with most of the farmsteads on the side of the road, fields stretching behind them, often with a ditch of water running through the property. Many of the farmhouses were separated from the road by an eight-foot dyke. The farms were all thinly wooded, and intensely cultivated. Occasionally a farmhouse had been bombed—but the land around was tended by other farmers —we rarely saw a neglected field. Before the war, the Dutch people ranked as one of the most hospitable in the world— neighbours taking the privilege of dropping in for a chat or a stein of home-brewed beer or schnapps at anytime—but now the farmhouses with ditches or moats between them and the road drew in the bridges and wrote no welcome on the mat, and that means you, Englishmen who can bring nothing but trouble! We had heard of the caves at St Pietersberg near Maastricht in which works of art and escaped allied prisoners were being hidden in that order in hundreds of miles of underground tunnels—but Maastricht was at least a hundred miles to the south-east and more difficult to get to than Brussels.

When Simon woke me to take my second turn on watch, he did not immediately settle down to sleep, but sat near me so we could whisper.

"How do you estimate our chances?"

He didn't want the placebo of 'Oh, we'll manage'. Jonfey would have been happy with the confident reply—Simon wanted diagnosis and treatment.

"It's impossible to estimate. Certainly we must keep ourselves up to pitch all the time—our escape will depend on being alert, seeing opportunities, and taking them when they come."

"Nothing constructive we can do?"

"Nothing I can think of—if you have any suggestions, I'd be glad to listen."

"You don't enjoy this command do you?" There was no impropriety in his suggestion, no insubordination.

"No, I don't. It's an artificial situation. I have no more information or knowledge than any one of you, and therefore no right to command you."

"But you have the inherent power of leadership . . ."

"Whatever that high-sounding phrase may mean!"

"You're a born leader!"

"Is there such a thing?"

"Churchill is a born leader—that's where the Americans go wrong—all their leaders are self-made men, and they usually make a mess of it! I have the education," Simon said, "to be a leader of men—you need to develop a pride when you spend your life looking down a cow's throat with the farmer relying on you for information—to the farmers you're a leader of men, a paragon. But that's in my specialised subject. The born leader has instinctive reasoning powers on all subjects. He knows that 'a hundred years after he's dead and forgotten, men who have never heard of him will be moving to the measure of his thought'."

"Oliver Wendell Holmes, 1809 to 1894. 'Moving to the measure', a lovely phrase!"

"See what I mean?"

I did see what he meant—the cunning devil was trying to bolster my ego, help me assume the mantle of leadership the better to serve them all. "There comes a time, Simon, when you abandon reason. You load your gun and cock it, with the safety catch off, and prepare to shoot over open sights. Don't worry—that's the way we all are at this moment—a little edgy perhaps, inclined to criticise and denigrate ourselves—but even without reason I believe we'll get out of here. Not all of us, perhaps, but most of us. And anyone left behind will be dead."

The first flicker of uncertainty crossed his face. Like all of us, he had been confident we would survive the long way home, and perhaps more perceptive than most had tried to help bolster my morale. But the law of averages was against us all getting through, just as it had been against us all jumping from that pipe. The law of averages works to close margins—there was no margin on that pipe, no margin now. One of us was already mathematically dead. But which one? It would take a crystal ball to know that. It would be simple to say Jonfey, since his had been the life of danger, chances taken. But Jonfey lived under his own law of averages and one day one chance taken would fail him—that separate issue, however, should not confuse our situation. Alone, each one of us might or might not get home, and the sum total could be any number between all home, or none. Together we had the law working with as well as against us. Some of us were bound to get through—that was as certain as the fact that all of us couldn't make it. Purely selfishly—I was glad we were sticking together.

"Ask yourself this question, Simon, an give me an honest answer. Would our chances of survival be increased if you take command? I'm perfectly prepared to abdicate and then to follow your leadership."

He thought for a moment—not the idling of the mind that many mistake for thought but a logical assessment of the pros and cons, factors for, factors against.

"I wanted to be absolutely certain," he said, "and now I am. You lead—that way we stand a better chance. You live in the country because you own a piece of it—it's your domain. I know the country because I've chosen to work there—none of it belongs to me and therefore I treat it with too much respect. Lead us over this bit of country as if you owned it, and we'll make it. If I take us through it, reticent and respectful as an employee, we'll be taken."

I sat through my watch, thinking of what Simon had said. Boldness was the key to our escape, boldness and confidnce. Dammit, we only had to walk ten miles, and before the war I usually walked that distance every day, and met twenty people who would touch a forelock to me, from respect not servitude. That spirit would get us through, if anything would.

It was time to waken the sergeant.

"The Dutch have opened the dykes in Zeeland—there'll be a helluva lot of water," he said, shortly after I woke him.

"It could help us."

"When I came down from Bergen we put into Rotterdam —I had a couple of days to spare before going down the Rhine to Dusseldorf and took a boat all round that north Zeeland coastline, south of the Hague. I met quite a few people round there—we might possibly look them up if ever we get there."

"We'll get there, don't worry."

"I'm not worrying—I don't give a damn where it hapens, here and now, falling off the side of a boat off Bergen in a northern storm, running about with a barrel of molten iron in a foundry. It's got to happen sometime, hasn't it?"

Damn him, I thought, fatalists never are the ones to get caught, and that increases the odds to one in three.

"Is there nothing and no-one you'd regret?"

"Yes, there are lots of things—mostly places I've never been to rather than things I've never done—I'd like to have seen Sumatra, and Borneo, and Honolulu—I'd like to have gone with the loggers in Canada, rolling down the rivers to the seaway. But people, well, you meet 'em and you leave 'em. They say all women are alike in bed under the blankets, and that's certainly true—but when you come down to it there's nothing of a challenge about the human race, is there? Some you like and some you don't like, but they don't really affect you, do they? Take this war—well, some people bust a gut over an ideal, but when it comes down to it, what does it mean? The natural instincts of men come to the top —the sadistic cruelty, the urge to destroy and kill. In other men it's the creative side—engineers build bridges, which is what they would have been doing in the first place, and administrative officers administer, which is exactly the same for them as it would be in civvie life, except that they're pushing the pen in some office in a foreign town, with no missis to look over their shoulders. The war is all a bloody misnomer, sir, if you'll pardon the expression. Here are we doing exactly what the elastic stocking-topped short-knickered leader of the scout troup would be doing on a long week-end with the boys in camp. We're planning to cover a stretch of ground without the artificial aids of modern so-called civilisation to help us—no trolley buses or underground trains or tramcars, no street lamps, no direction boards to guide us. So where's the difference? The only difference, as far as I can see, is that some great hulking hairy-arsed German might come charging out of a brush at us. But if ever you'd walked down Sauchiehall Street on a Saturday night, you'd know that a hairy-arsed Glaswegian lurks in every doorway, and they'll slit the cobblers off you for the price of a bottle of meths. Look at that," he said. He pulled his shirt free of his trousers. I had seen the scar before when he had been stripped for washing in North Wales, but had never asked him its origin. "I got that on the waterfront in Bergen—and it's a damn sight worse than Jonfey's little lot. I was with a bird in bed, and her boy-friend tried to stick a broken bottle up my arse! That was in peacetime! So where's all the fuss about the war?"

"And Miss Rosenberg?" I ought not to have said that. He was on some private journey of justification—and it was my duty to let each of the men prepare his own palliatives for our present plight. But I wanted no illusions—only cold hard reality and facing facts would get us out of there; reality, and a constant state of preparation.

"That's different," he said, sullen.

"I suppose the Sicilian vendettas are different, and the gangsters in Chicago, and the Brighton racegoers, and the Russian revolution—they're all different, I suppose?"

"That's different," he said again.

I got up and walked round our encampment in the copse. It was dusk, time to go. We woke Jonfey, who was obviously much better for the sleep. His wound, too, was less flushed, less angry. There was a dyke about five hundred yards further on, and moored to the side of the canal a long boat. I was tempted to take it, but it had a name on the side and would be known throughout the waterway. Any Dutchman seeing us in that boat would know it stolen—and there would be foes among the friends. The Dutch came of German stock—in some of them it increased the hatred—but many have never forgiven the British for past enmities, and would have preferred to stay as neutral in this world war as in the last. Their homeland had been wrested, acre by acre, from the sea, giving the Dutch a fierce pride in their own achievements. Now, because of British political ineptitude and German cries of Lebensraum, much of that hard reclaimed land had been reinundated, given back to the sea from whence it came. There was no Dutch door-knocking for us!

We travelled fast throughout most of that night. Frequently we had to make detours because of water barriers or the movement of German troops—there still appeared to be much activity in that area, and several artillery batteries were being moved west towards the coast.

A battalion of infantry came marching down the road. We nipped into the farm to the side of the road, over a narrow water break, into an orchard keeping apart among the orderly lines of trees. An orchard is a deceptive place in which to stalk. The trees in line are impenetrable to the eye, until you take another pace forward and suddenly look down an open lane which could contain a whole squadron of tanks. Walking along the edge of an orchard, with the lateral lines, and the diagonal lines meeting and separating as you walk—what Lorca calls the opening and closing of a fan—is a most eerie experience. A company of men had bivouaced at the other side of the orchard. The infantry had halted behind us. Ahead of us was a deep twenty-foot wide dyke, and behind us the farmhouse, occupied by soldiers. We were trapped. Damn! Damn! Damn! Down on your belly and into the sparse undergrowth—here's a farmer keeps his grass cut under the trees—blast the careful husbandry of Dutch smallholders. And blast too the searchlight beam of the moon, which at that moment came out in pristine glory.

Jonfey crawled to the water. Not a hope of getting across —there's a long boat lapping the edge with two men sitting in the prow, with nothing to do but look down the length and dream fishermen's dreams. Sergeant back to the road— not a hope, the infantry have bivouaced in the field on the other side of the road which now looks like Piccadilly on a Saturday night. Simon to the other edge—no chance, the company is on stand-to and it's like the Northampton County Show out there—all that's missing is the ice-cream stall!

I crawled slowly through the grass to the farmhouse. The orchard ended a hundred yards this side of it. I could see duty officers in the farmhouse doorway, smoking and talking together. Behind the farm a long barn, and a beast yard. Beyond a small field, oddly enough, of barley. They don't grow much barley in this part of Holland, I thought—this was the first crop I had seen. The whole farm and its surroundings, bathed in bright moonlight that sharpens outlines and bleaches colours, reminded me of one of these early Dutch paintings of scene—a Franz Hals perhaps before he became obsessed by rapid smiling faces. It would be just possible to get down the track at the side of the house and into and through the barn and beast yard into the barley field, but impossible, quite impossible, to travel the hundred yards to the start of the track unseen. It was a moment for quick decisions. A barrel of fruit-tree spray stood on a stand at the edge of the orchard. I whispered to Simon, Jonfey and the sergeant to hoist it onto their shoulders. Jonfey had kept the cap of the German in the Mercedes tucked in his epaulette. I put it on though it was far too small for me. "If it were done, 'tis better it were done quickly," I whispered to Simon, who smiled at me. I marched the men out of the orchard, along its side, turned them left and marched them straight across the hundred yards patch towards the barn. Our heads were concealed by the barrel, though I walked to the rear and occasionally fell back half a pace to observe the two officers talking in the rose-trellised doorway. As we marched along, links recht, links recht, I saw the sergeant break out in a thick sweat. So it did matter—he did care that it should not be here and now! As we marched, to create that mood of unquestioning reality, I growled at them, in quiet German, "Kommen Sie, wachsen Sie auf, machen Sie schnell, der Leutnant uns erwartet." The officers did not glance in our direction; I had the safety catch off the driver's Luger, and the boys were poised to drop the barrel and dash into that field of barley. The track leading to the barn drew ever nearer—twenty, fifteen, ten paces, when suddenly, one of the officers became aware of our presence. I had over-done the commands—they had intruded on his conscious-ness—"which officer was waiting for us, and why?" But quickly he dismissed the matter.

"Schweigen-Sie!" he called. "Haben Sie den Befehl nicht gelesen?"

"Jawohl, Herr Kapitan," I muttered, and shut up as he had requested. Five paces to go. I couldn't know, of course, that he was a Captain—if he turned out to be a major, as pompous as many I'd met, we would be in trouble. My finger tightened on the trigger, but already he was talking again to the other officer and ignored us. I prayed at this last moment none of the lads would trip, or do anything to arouse interest. Three paces to go, two, and one, and straight up the track into the barn. Here we could relax, if only for a few seconds. As they put it down, the barrel spilled ammoniacal spray over them—at least they wouldn't be bothered by mosquitos when we reached the delta.

The sergeant looked at me when we had got back our nerve and I nodded. "Right lads, into the barley with you, RV in the far corner."

There comes a time when you've had enough—when your spirit rebels and refuses to cringe. I had crawled far enough. "Follow me," I said, and marched out of the door, head high, arms swinging, dead regimental. The boys unhesitat-ingly followed me. Anyone seeing us coming from that barn, attached to the headquarters' house, would assume that we too were official, provided we retained a confident mien to help persuade them. And, dammit, I was angry, and confi-dent. My knees were sore from scraping on the ground, my arms ached from pulling me along. I was dirty, dusty, un-clean. We marched out of that barn, with spirits uncon-quered. "Left right left"—though no-one was there with a pacing stick to call it, and we're off to see the Wizard, the wonderful Wizard of Oz, and over there are the subdued lights of the mess and a couple of gins and tonics before din-ner, and a bath and change into clean linen. Three men ap-peared in the gloaming—they were marching, as we were from a known place to a known destination. Seeing my stride, they withdrew in the dark to very edge of the track. "Danke," I said, "und gute Nacht."

"Goodnight, sir," the corporal in charge of them said, respectfully keeping his gaze averted. We marched straight past them, in single file up the side of the barley field, Hannibal crossing the Alps, 'all the King's men, marching up the hill and never, never back again!' At the far side of the field the Germans had stored ammunition in a small hut. Certainly they would have spotted us had we been crawling. As it was the two men unloading the flat barrow hardly gave us a look as we marched along.

We had come from the headquarters in full moonlight, erect and walking determinedly to a destination that wasn't their concern. That was good enough for them. "Achtung!" I said, and they moved the barrow to one side to let us past.

Simon drew level with me when we had left the barley field behind. "Do you see what I mean," he whispered. "I would never have dared do that, yet the tone in your voice was perfect when you spoke to those men."

"My knees were knocking—I thought they must hear them!"

"Your knees may have been knocking—mine certainly were, but your voice didn't quaver as mine would have done. Now walk us over to England!"

By ten o'clock, largely by boldness, we reached the delta of the Maas. The low stretch of water below sea level that reaches out to the sea like a crooked beckoning finger, the northernmost polder of Nord Brabant with Willemstad on the far side, was on our left. To the right, though we couldn't see it, was Doordrecht—beyond that Rotterdam. All that stood between us and the North Sea was the long curving channel of the estuary of the Maas, a distance of forty miles.

It would be a long swim.

The sergeant stood beside me as I gazed out over the water. Somehow the forty miles didn't seem so far, after all.

"Shall we try the land, or the water?" he asked. I think he would have preferred to stay on land where he would have felt less exposed, but I wanted to get out on the water, to get my belly off the ground. That channel invited me, the water flowing along it was going somewhere. "What do you think, Jonfey?" I could see the sergeant felt snubbed since I had asked one of the others. "Knock off a boat and let's get to hell out of here!" Jonfey said.

"You can see a boat a mile off!" the sergeant said.

It was even chances the channel would be blocked at Willemstad and possibly again at Middelharnis, but it was a good mile wide even at its narrowest point—a boat low down would be practically invisible from the shore at ground level.

We soon found the boat we were looking for—a flat-bottomed barge a farmer used to shift crops. Twenty feet long and only four wide, there was an inboard engine mounted at the back and a long low hold in which most recently potatoes had been carried. The three dozen small ones left in the corners we devoured. Sitting to the back of the boat two men, one at each side, could paddle it comfortably and quite swiftly though I wouldn't rely on making too much speed in tidal waters. We headed for the centre of the waterway, the sergeant and Simon taking first turn on the paddles we found in a forward locker. The boat name *Gruedel* was new to me—though Dutchmen have a style of humour all of their own.

It was a long night—a night of sliding motion through the water, the slap of the paddles and the trickle of wavelets against the curved prow of the boat. From time to time motorised vessels rode past us but we were too low to be seen. The early bright moon had clouded—there was just sufficient light to distinguish the dark mass of landfall on each side of us and the motors of the other boats throbbed ample warning of their presence. Once a large boat came streaking down the centre of the estuary looking ridiculously high for such a channel. We pulled rapidly into the bank when we heard its engines, and waited until it had passed. We could have been visible from its high decks—a dark spot on a sheen of water where no dark spots ought to be. We didn't speak since sound carries over water, and innumerable birds came to investigate us—teal, mallard, ducks of various species. It must have been a wonderful stretch of water for shooting over, before the war. The irony of the thought struck me—with all these Germans about, it could be so again though this time we'd be targets not hunters. For a little while I slept sitting in the hold with my back against the gunwhale, but I awoke in anxious fear. Though the day had been warm the night on the water was cold and terrifying shapes of mist came sliding towards us like some phantom amphibian.

From time to time we passed an active encampment and once were directly in line of fire when an anti-aircraft unit discharged all its guns—the noise thumped our eardrums and for minutes afterwards I heard nothing. The whirr whirr of the shells over our heads, just before the crack and thump of the guns, stayed sickeningly with me in that deafness. If one of those shells had been short fused we would have been in line to receive it in our laps, and would never have heard it.

Then came the dawn across the low long flat land, especially spectacular. Alone on the water we were tempted to think it might be entirely for our benefit. The first highly

coloured rays of light in fierce reds and ochres and yellows
of flame shot as suddenly as our train explosion, as if com-
pressed beyond the horizon and suddenly tossed like spar-
kling dice. I dared not gaze at it—I had a night watch to
keep. After the first startling rays, night seemed to creep back
if only for a minute or two and the bursts of spent light
spread slowly over the skyline, fighting for a foothold. The
banks were thrown into shadow south of us—more difficult
than ever to look for the waiting marksman. I wanted to
cling to the concealing night, but knew the hope forlorn.
We would have to pull in somewhere. As we paddled along
the banks of the Maas lightened and we passed through a
thickly populated area. Along the banks the farms lay silent under this grey ill-lit dawning. Where the soil level was
raised above the dykes trees grew, beech, oak, some poplar,
willow and elm. Here was not much of the fir forest in which
we had walked most of the night through vaulted caverns of
gloom. Along the banks everything seemed small—farms lay
close together, with small orchards. When the first sunlight
began to appear we pulled to the north coast and paddled
close to the bank looking for suitable shelter. Now it was my
turn to take the helm; in the two hours we must have covered
nine miles or so and my shoulders said so vigorously. Dykes
were to the north of us, and a reclaimed lake, a polder, dropped three feet below the level of the water we were traversing.
Soon we came to what seemed a small tributary of the Maas.
Ten feet across its mouth was overgrown with willow and
poplar. We went in under the branches; it was a small inland
pond about two hundred feet in diameter surrounded entirely by trees. Despite the effort involved we dragged the
boat out of the water under a tree; heavy going but necessary
concealment. Since we had not allowed Jonfey to take any
part in the rowing he had slept on the boat and took first
watch. Simon and the sergeant settled down to sleep; but
too wide awake I walked round the perimeter of the wood
to see where we were. I was desperately hungry, though for
bacon and eggs, not raw potatoes. I wanted something stim-
ulating in hot water—ever ersatz coffee. More than anything else the lack of salt and sugar gets you most, and warm
food and liquids. Even the most rudimentary food is elevated
when heated and seasoned or sweetened.

The wood was part of a farm. The farmhouse about five
hundred yards away didn't seem to be occupied by troops.
An ack-ack battery about a mile and a half the other side of
the farm doubtless protected the southern run to Rotterdam
and I could see the smoke of the cookhouse fires of military

units dotting the plain. There appeared to be nothing near
this particular farm. Doubtless they felt the R.A.F. would
take the waterway of the Maas as a route in, turn left at
Willemstad straight up to Rotterdam, bombs away, then out
over the Zuiderzee, the North Sea and home. This farm
would be under the turning point—an impossible location
from which to fire an ack-ack gun. This route would also
serve as a corridor to the Ruhr, which accounted for the
heavy concentration of bigger guns we had seen on our way
out, and the extensive troop movements. There had been
activity beyond the skyline during the night, but too far for
me to identify its origin.*

I suddenly felt an irresistible attraction to that farm. It
was foolish to break cover, stupid in the circumstances, but
truly I could not resist. A thin wisp of smoke was spiralling
lazily skywards from the chimney—the stove beneath would
be banked down with wood ash for the night. Within a half
hour or so, the farmer and his wife would arise, prise open
the top of the gackle and stir it to life with the bundle of
brushwood from the box she kept beside the stove in her neat
kitchen. Despite the shortages of the war, there'd be a side
of pork somewhere and she'd cut off a slice for the farmer
to eat with coffee before setting out on a day's work in the
fields. There were cattle behind the farmhouse—doubtless
the Germans counted every head but he'd be a poor farmer
if he couldn't fix a headcount. Chickens too were penned
beyond the house so there would be eggs! Cows for milk, butter, cheese, and cream. My mouth was wet with saliva.

Also I needed to use an indoor lavatory. I needed to sit
there with a locked door and three walls between me and
the rest of the world, then use paper, not leaves!

I waited for the sudden spurt of smoke from the chimney
before walking out of the wood into the farmyard. The door
opened from inside, the farmer standing in stockinged feet.
I noticed the three pairs of wooden shoes on the doorstep.
His baggy trousers were held up by cotton braces, and a
woollen shirt open at the neck was designed to take a separate collar though doubtless he never wore one during the
week. He exuded that wonderful odour of feather beds and
food. His wife was revealed in the door behind him.

I spoke to him in German. "Good morning. Can I come
in?"

"Are you English?"

---

* It came from Arnhem and Nijmegen, as war historians will
have guessed.

"No, French. I'm lost."

"Come in," he said. His wife made a noise of protest, which ended as he carefully shut the door behind me. "There are Germans everywhere," he said—he hadn't believed my story about being French, but wasn't going to make an issue of it. "They come every day."

"What do you want?" his wife asked, her fear quickly gone.

"Coffee?"

"Ja," she said, and went and got me a mug from the dresser at the side of the door. She filled it with coffee from an enamelled jug on top of the stove. "French," she said—she meant the coffee, not me. If it was French coffee then I was a Dutchman, but it tasted like nectar. "The German soldiers come for eggs—they bring coffee and cigarettes," the farmer said, quick to establish his status. He was a good collaborator, and not ashamed of it, a practical man making the best of the circumstances. "They let me keep the farm—I have a bad heart. I'm going to die at any moment, that's what the specialist says in Rotterdam." His opinion of the specialist from Rotterdam would not be fit to print, to judge from his expression. Certainly he looked blue about the lips if you examined his face closely, but that could be the sun and the coast-line salt.

"Are you alone?" he asked.

"No, there are three others with me." In for a penny, in for a pound.

I drank deeply of the coffee, my eyes attracted unavoidably by the pan of pork and potatoes on the top of the stove, the loaf of brown bread, the pot of butter on the table.

"Come," the farmer said, and sat down at the table. His wife put a plate in front of me, another in front of him, and we started to eat. The food was deliciously hot and I emptied the plate. His wife brought a big sausage from a cupboard behind an open larder—it was farm made, similar to the black puddings that were such a part of Yorkshire life before the war. She cut two thick slices and put them in the frying pan, one for me, one for the farmer. I ate my slice too quickly—he was still mopping the pork fat with his bread. He lifted the slice from his plate and passed it to me. Though ashamed of my greed, I ate it.

"You spent the night in a long boat," he said. When I looked puzzled he laughed. "Any Dutchman from these parts knows the reek of longboats at potato time. Did you steal it?"

"Borrowed it."

"That means hardship for the farmer."

"I know that. I regret it, but there was no alternative."

"You come from inland?"

"Yes."

"And you are going," he flexed his thumb over his shoulder, "that way, to England?"

"Hoffentlich?"

"It would be a long night's walk without the boat."

His wife was standing by the stove, looking at me. When she saw I had observed her, she turned away and busied herself at the top of the stove. "You'll have to forgive her," the farmer said. "You're the first one she's seen. Her sister had an airman in Waalwijk. He was recaptured."

"That's not true," his wife burst in, family pride getting the better of her. "No, he wasn't recaptured. He was so badly burned they could do nothing for him. To save his life they surrendered him to the Germans." The farmer shrugged his shoulders.

"And was that not a good thing to do?" the woman asked me. It had obviously been a family squabble since the day it happened, one of those inconsequential seeds of dissension that green-manure a marriage.

"I'm certain it was the best thing to do," I reassured her. The farmer had no need of me to take his point of view.

He had the peasant strength of the earth about him—a man with an allotted life-span as finite as the seasons. "You live where you stand and lie where you fall," he said. "God sows, God reaps, but the pigs make the fertiliser!"

I could like this man—I felt as safe as at home.

"Can you help us? All we want is a bed for the day, food and something hot to drink, and we'll be on our way as soon as it becomes dark."

"Your men are in the wood, of course, and you've pulled the boat up the bank, I hope?"

"Yes."

"Good. The water patrols start at eight o'clock, and the first scrounging bastard of a soldier comes about ten o'clock asking for eggs. I can't permit you all to sleep in the house of course, but you are welcome to the barn. If you're caught, I'll look you straight in the eye, and as in days of old will say 'No, I have never seen him before.' I may revile you, and spit on you, and dance when they nail you to a cross, but that will be for my wife—you understand."

"I understand." I was grateful and had no words with which to express it—I asked his name, but he preferred not to give it lest under torture I blurt it out.

"It will be good to do something for a change," he said.
"All day long I sit on the farm, looking at my steaming
muck heap, building up goodness for the future which doubtless I shall not see and would not want anyway if the Allies
are beaten in this war. It will be good to do something for a
change!"

He put on his jacket and we left the farm together. I
went back to the woods and brought Jonfey, Simon and
the sergeant separately. When we arrived and I saw to their
concealment, the farmer's wife came to the door of the barn.

"Bring them into the kitchen first," she said. "There'll be
no-one about for some time, and my husband is in the lower
field."

Though feeling somewhat guilty I brought the men inside
and they ate a pan full of pork, sausage and bread, and
drank coffee with the black sugar she stored concealed in a
sack in the barn. In peacetime the sugar had been used for
feeding bees and cider-making, but we were glad of it. Then
I saw them settled into the barn, comfortable for the day.
Eggs in one basket! I had resolved despite the temptations to
lie in the wood keeping observation, but the farmer's wife
was most persuasive, and I spent the morning in her kitchen.
It was a safe place from which to watch—every time I saw
anyone approach I nipped through into the sitting room,
from the window of which I could make my way round the
back of the farm unobserved. We didn't talk much during
the morning—she told me about her sister and the airman
—apparently she had done all she could to get him well again
and only in desperation had taken him and left him where
the Germans were sure to find him. Though the Germans
could see he had been tended, they exacted no reprisals.

"I think she fell a little bit in love with him, nicht wahr?"
the farmer's wife said, with a shy look. I had no fears, she
was old enough to be my mother.

At lunch time the farmer came back to the farmhouse
to eat his midday meal—he was not surprised to find me in
the farmhouse. "She has a most persuasive tongue," he said,
smiling at his wife, "and I knew she would welcome someone to talk her nonsense to." Together we ate a meal fit for
Gargantua—ertwensoep—a rich thick pea soup—Zeeland
oysters, stewed smoked eel, and a plate of potatoes and sauer-
kraut, with farmhouse cheese. After I had eaten, the farmer's
wife persuaded me to go upstairs and sleep on the bed that
had belonged to their son, now married on his own farm at
Gennep. Wounded during the invasion he had only recently

come from hospital in 's-Hertogenbosch—he'd lost the use of an arm and found the forty acres difficult to manage.

The sergeant by now was awake and took over my vigil in the kitchen. I was determined not to be caught again.

We were all awake by the early evening. We sat in the kitchen with the farmer and his wife, drank his homebrewed beer and talked. Mostly we talked of England, not of the war—about farms and farming, animal husbandry, crop-planting methods, types of seeds sown, fertilisers used. I could see the sergeant and Jonfey were bored with our conversation, but for a while I was determined to break the pattern of war, if only within the sanctuary of those four walls. More than anything, the Dutchman was proud of the way they had reclaimed land—the system of dykes, the use of the water to increase fertility. On his farm were more than two thousand square feet of greenhouse in which he had grown daffodils and other flowers in peacetime. "I'll never see them in bloom again, that is certain," he said, though without any self-pity. During this brief return to sanity, we listened to music on the radio, discussed songs and singers. We heard the local news from Amsterdam and Hilversum, Paris and Brussels. When Jonfey wanted to tune in to London, however, the farmer wouldn't do so. "One risk at a time is enough," he drily said. He was quite right—the sudden thud of the knocker on the door sent us all flying, our beer mugs quickly seized off the table and taken with us.

The German soldier was drunk. He wanted eggs. The farmer told him there were no eggs—he was telling the truth, we had eaten them for supper, the farmer's wife laughing to see the way we boiled them—she had never seen anyone eat a boiled egg before. The farmer led the German out to the 'egg factory', as jokingly he called it. The soldier's companion was sitting on the seat of the motor-cycle combination —he too appeared to be drunk. The farmer opened the mesh door of the chicken run and told the German he could take any eggs he could find. Luckily, two had been laid since the last collection and the drunken soldier went away happily with them. "He'll break them before he gets back to barracks," the farmer said. "Let's hope they are in his pocket at the time!"

By ten o'clock it was time to leave—I had been on edge for the past hour feeling we had outstayed our welcome, every second we enjoyed the farmer's hospitality another we kept them in danger. But somehow it felt as if we had left England a hundred years ago, instead of only a few brief hours, and the joy of civilisation was a benison. How fortunate the continental people are to enjoy a literate working class—the farmer had discoursed with us all evening on many topics—he was interested and interesting, far more civilised than his English counterpart would have been—or many men in England who ranked as his social superiors among the white-collar classes. The sergeant had knocked about the world—and spoke German with a vulgar fluency. The Dutch peasant spiced his evening's conversation with Schiller, Thomas Mann, Goethe, had a liberality of expression I greatly envied. He apologised for not being able to speak English, but made up for it, and entertained us vastly, by quoting Shakespeare in the Goethe translation—mocking the Shakespearian actor Alexander Moise, whose 'Sein, oder nicht sein, das ist die Frage', was every bit as good a rendition as that of Henry Irving. I had both recordings at home in my youth—and had not dreamed to hear them both discussed in this surrounding. Image or reality—what had the sergeant said about the war; it gave many of us the opportunity to do things we had never hoped to be able to do.

"You will forgive me, I know, that I step aside in this war," the farmer said, as we were about to leave. "I am not neutral, like so many of my countrymen. I do not like what the Germans are doing. I do not like aggression or any of the stinking sludge that inevitably must follow in its wake. But I am conscious my life is coming to a close, and so far have not found anything to value more than that flickering flame soon to be extinguished." He came with us as far as the wood, treading surely before us through the gloaming, across these few acres into which he had poured his entire being. He couldn't help us lift the boat from under the trees, but supervised our efforts to manhandle it down the slope.

We had got it half way down the bank, its prow touching the surface of the water, when the German motor boat in the trees at the entrance started its engine and came into full view. The sailor in the prow switched on the beam of a searchlight and we were trapped.

"Hände hoch," the sailor behind him called, as the boat edged into the bank.

There was nothing we could do.

We raised our hands and I turned around to warn Jonfey of the futility of attempting anything in the face of the machine gun mounted on the roof of the cabin. There was no sign of the old Dutch farmer.

"Damn!" I thought, "Damn!" I think I hated the thought of deceit more than that of betrayal. Obviously the Judas wanted to get us out of the house before we were taken—

didn't want the disorder in his own home should we decide to put up a fight for it. Out here in the woods, his precious homestead was safe. Damn! Damn! Doubtless there was a unit of the SS, alerted by him during the day, creeping up behind us through the wood. No wonder he led us here! He wanted to make quite certain we didn't change our minds and try to escape overland. If only he hadn't spent the evening talking so civilly with us—'to be or not to be' left a significantly dirty taste in my mouth just now.

Simon's hand on my back pocket slid to the side towards the Luger in the pistol holder hanging from a button on my denim jacket near the sliver of glass. The Germans couldn't see the movement of his hand. I turned my body round, slightly, to help conceal the pistol. Pray to God one of them doesn't count hands in what must look like a small forest of hands raised to the sky. I felt the stud come loose, the sudden shift of weight as the Luger was withdrawn from the holster. The German boat was now at the edge of the water about thirty feet from us. There were four men on board, one in the tiny wheelhouse aft had been steering the boat, another on the gunwhales with a boat hook pulled the boat alongside the bank. The other on top of the wheelhouse behind a tripod-mounted and lashed machine gun, magazine fed, rate of fire one hundred to the minute on rapid, thirty on slow, with an accurate fore and aft sight of crossed wires, had his finger on the trigger. We had fired those machine guns on the range at Rhayader; on rapid rate they were so accurate they could tear the centre out of a four inch thick timber target in seconds; on slow rate with time to aim you could put three shots into a cigarette packet at a hundred yards, and we were only thirty feet away.

The fourth man standing in the prow squatted with his hands on a ten-inch diameter searchlight. Luckily the searchlight aimed low at our feet and we could see through the halo of its upper rim as they intended that flight or resistance would be futile.

If we didn't attempt anything, they had no intention of shooting. Not yet, anyway.

Through the corner of my eye I saw the plop into the water as if of a large water rat, and the ripples made a pattern with those of the gently rocking boat. Now they had us the Germans seemed undetermined what to do with us. The sailor in charge of the wheel came forward and conferred in undertones with the man behind the machine gun. They appeared to be having a discussion—if not, in fact, an argument. I hoped it was not, 'To shoot or not to shoot,

that is the question!' The navigator went back into the
wheelhouse and searched through sheets of official message
pads. Eventually, he came across the one he wanted and
showed it to the man behind the gun. He looked up at each
in turn, identifying us.

The old farmer was swimming in the water on the other
side of the boat, moving without sound though I could see
he was not a good swimmer.

The man at the machine gun convinced the navigator
and the argument ended with him taking aim through the
backsight of the gun.

Then he half rose in the air, gurgled, twisted and fell off
the boat, the handle of a kitchen-knife sticking out of his
back. Simon took a half pace to the right, beside me, and
picked off the navigator, the man with the boat hook, the
man behind the light and finally, as it swung skywards, the
light itself.

By that time I was at the water's edge. It took us five
minutes to find the old farmer, since the water had logged
his clothing.

We took him back to the farm and undressed him, put on
his night garments and laid him in his bed. Simon told us
that, since his heart had stopped with the strain of hurling
that knife up into the machine-gunner's back, there would
be no water in the lungs. He was known to be medically
unsound, and the Germans would take no notice of his death.
His wife sat on the chair in the kitchen, mute and immobile
while we laid her husband's body to rest in their marriage
bed. She had forgiven us.

"I will go to my son at Gennep," she kept saying. "He
needs someone to help him, and I have my permit to travel."

When we had finished and could find no reason for staying other than to console her, she looked across the kitchen
to me. "He didn't like it when my sister gave that airman
to the Germans," she said, "for the life of him, he couldn't
agree with that!"

Early that evening, her husband had quoted to us a few
lines from a poet Lilienthal, of whom we hadn't heard.
"Laengst schon dein Grab die Winde ueberwehen; wie
liebevoll du sorgtest"—and for a long time the winds would
blow over *his* grave, and how full of love *he* would seem.

Still I didn't know his name.

CHAPTER TWELVE

Jonfey's wound had taken a turn for the worse. Whether it was the day of comfortable living, the rich food we had eaten, or a delayed action, no-one could tell, but when Simon took off his dressing to make a routine check, the edges of the wound had blanched almost white, and the festering centre was of greenish yellow. The pain, Jonfey finally confessed, had been intense for the last hour. Simon felt up under his armpit and beckoned to me. "Feel that," he said. In the centre of the armpit was a lump the size of a swallow's egg, hard.

I had only one of the morphine pills left.

"Save it," Simon said, "he may need it later."

I haven't spoken much about Jonfey in the course of this tale, largely because there wasn't much to say about him. His unfailing good humour had been a wonderful stimulant to us all—his constant eagerness and his chirpy turns of phrase. Jonfey successfully bridged the gap between Simon, myself, and the sergeant—he was the butt of the sergeant's regimentation and could respond to the ram-rod-backed discipline without losing his senses of proportions. Yet he had a head about him, and his keen intellect put him a yard ahead of the sergeant. The sergeant was a 'do-er'—a man of immense courage and physical strength, great resourcefulness. He could interpret commands well and swiftly. Jonfey also was a 'do-er' but he thought more about things than did the sergeant—hadn't the same instinct for blind obedience. Sometimes, of course, he could be frustrating beyond measure; so often his interpretation of orders was so much superior to the orders themselves. The sergeant would ask permission before changing an order; Jonfey would go ahead and do it in his own version and tell you of the change later. This of course could be very difficult dependent as we were on complete co-ordination, but I had no wish to lose him. I looked closely at his face. There was strain at the corner of his eyes, bloodshot lines on the pupils. "That side's been hurting you for some time, hasn't it?" I insisted.

"It has a bit."

"You're a fool—you ought to have told Simon."

"The bloody horse doctor? He's no good without a bottle of liniment and a dose of jollop!" There was good humour in his face, despite the pain. I could see he had not wished to disturb Simon, lacking, as he was, any practical medical aid. I resolved never again to drop into any assignment without a full medical kit concealed about my person.

"Is there anything we can do, Simon?" I asked.

"Nothing unless we go back to the farmhouse."

"We can't do that," Jonfey said quickly. "That'd be pushing our luck too far."

I looked at the sergeant, and at Simon. It would be dangerous to go back to the farm.

"I know what we could do," Jonfey said, a smile breaking across his face—"it's old fashioned, but it used to work a treat, so they say."

"What's that?"

"Pig muck! It draws like a magnet. It smells like hell, of course, but it was always used for infections. You'll never get a diseased horse in a field that's kept pigs! There's a field of pigs just outside this wood; I bet the sergeant could get us a handful and no-one the wiser, couldn't you, Sergeant?"

"Would it work?" I asked Simon.

"Yes, I suppose it could, come to think of it."

"Could it do him any harm—infect him with any fever?"

"I don't think so—no, anyway, the infection already inside him is bad enough."

The sergeant crawled away on his errand of mercy. When he returned he had brought back sufficient to medicate a small army! And he stank!

"You smear it on the wound," Simon said. "There's no point in both of us suffering!"

He bandaged the wound over the poultice, though the adhesive on the plaster no longer held, and he had to tear strips off the bottom of Jonfey's shirt to make a bandage to go all round his body.

"That should throb like hell!" he said to Jonfey. "If it doesn't, for God sake tell me, and we'll think of something else!"

I had been thinking of something else. How the devil were we to get home? That wound turning septic put a different complexion on our journey. Now, speed was essential. I didn't want to have to surrender Jonfey to the Germans to save his life and, though I had scant medical knowledge, the look on Simon's face when he asked me to feel the lump under Jonfey's armpit was enough to warn me of the danger if Jonfey soon didn't get expert treatment and proper medicine.

"Gather round," I said, when the bandaging had been completed. They settled down around me. "We have to get home quickly and I want your best thoughts on it before I make a decision. We can't hang about here—though that boat hadn't a radio, it won't be long before it's missed and they send someone looking for it. Also, now the farmer's dead, the Germans will run all over this property seeing what they can scrounge. That woman won't stay in the farmhouse longer than she needs to. I wouldn't be surprised if she packs up first thing in the morning and gets as best she can to her son's farm at Gennep. She's in a state of shock and anything could happen."

"If this pigshit doesn't work," Jonfey said, "you'll have to leave me behind. No hard feelings, you understand!"

"We shan't do that," I assured him, "unless it becomes absolutely necessary to save your life. There's no point in beating about the bush; you're a sick man and could become a liability, but we'll all happily bear that liability however onerous it may become, unless your life is in danger." I turned to the other two. "I presume I speak for us all?"

"Don't worry, lad," the sergeant said immediately. "If you can't walk I'll carry you out!" He meant it and could do it.

"We could take that boat and make a dash for it, straight across the North Sea to Harwich," Simon said. It was a question more than a statement. I had worked out that, with that boat and sufficient fuel, we could make it to England— in land terms the boat would do five miles an hour, I guessed, in the open sea, and take a gallon to every ten miles. "Harwich, due west of us, along the fifty-second parallel, is almost a hundred and thirty miles away. The trip could take the better part of thirty hours," I said.

"If we could sail straight without a compass," Jonfey added.

"I could do that," Simon said. "I've done a bit of sailing from stars."

"If we could get through the minefields at the mouth of this estuary," the sergeant said.

"One of us would have to swim ahead of the boat and we'd crawl through," Simon said.

"If we don't meet any German shipping, and if we can get hold of sufficient fuel and if we don't get blown out of the water by the Harwich coastal defences. Let's face it, there are a lot of ifs," I said. There was no point in false confidence.

"Why don't we forget the boat?" Jonfey said. "Over there are a dozen German units. Why don't we find a signals headquarters, knock it off, ring up Braintree, and ask them to send an aeroplane?"

"Just like that?" Simon was smiling.

It had the germ of a good idea.

"Yes, just like that! Dammit!" Jonfey said, "that's what we are trained to do. Are you forgetting that? We're bloody specialised miracle men. We're supposed to be able to rub our faces with burned cork which makes us invisible, and walk into anywhere we want. Isn't that what the Captain trained us to do?"

He was right. That was exactly the way I trained them. These were boys of the special services—trained to jump or sail in and get out again in one piece. That's what we here for, after all!

Jonfey had sold us. I knew which I would rather have, a fast trip back through the flak, or a long slow ride in an open boat with everything and everybody against us on both sides of the North Sea. In a German boat we'd be sitting ducks when we tried to slip into Harwich—I had the arrogant Anglo-Saxon belief our coastal defences would be a darned sight better than the Germans. I was more certain of getting out of Holland than into England.

"You stay here, Jonfey, on your own. If we're not back by morning, walk down that road and give yourself up. Is that clearly understood?"

"Yes, Captain!" I didn't believe a syllable.

"And you can amuse yourself by getting rid of those Germans."

"Yes, Captain!"

The sergeant, Simon and I skirted the farmhouse and set off down the side of the track. Then, as the first sign of an encampment drew near, we left the track and went into the fields. The first unit we came to, another ack-ack unit, we passed without difficulty. Now that we were in the German lines, we could see the concentration. In a sense it helped us, because with so many people about no-one was going to look too suspiciously at us. We spent most of our time, therefore, walking erect, and only dropped down to the ground when we needed to get past a tight encampment. I was looking for a radio aerial, a high one. Finally we saw one above a pantechnicon, parked in a corner of a field. The radio mast was at least forty feet high, supported by guy ropes down to the ground on each side of the truck. Other trucks around the field had smaller aerials above them. The trucks were widely separated—no doubt as a precaution against bombing. Near one of the other trucks, a number of vehicles were parked, and there appeared to be more activity. No-one however came to or went from the pantechnicon. We stayed in the grass at the edge of the field for an hour, watching. Several tents were pitched under the hedges on each of two arms stretched at right angles to the pantechnicon's position. At midnight exactly, four men came from one of the tents—larger than the others and obviously a mess hall—and climbed the steps into the radio truck.

"Changing duty operators," I whispered.

Sure enough, four or five minutes later four operators came from the pantechnicon and went across to the mess hall. One stopped on the way to relieve himself. The tents were lit with a pale blueish light—though a strict blackout was evidently enforced.

Simon had been studying the roof of the vehicle. "Three transmitters in there," he said. "Big job—probably goes back to Germany—smaller job on the dipole, probably goes to local units, and a short-distance rod job—probably for inter-camp communication. There'll also be telephone lines. One man for each set, one man on the telephone or switchboard, also doubling as maintenance mechanic."

At that moment a motor-cycle combination, with no-one in the side-car came into the field and stopped outside the pantechnicon. The driver switched off and went inside— when he came out again he ignored the motor-cycle and crossed to the mess tent. Now we could see a wisp of smoke coming from the far end of the tent, and I could taste the coffee.

"That'll be our problem," the sergeant said—"despatch riders—we'll never know when one will arrive."

We located the sentries. The camp had a manned perimeter through which we had passed on our stomachs, but no men actually on guard on the inside, in this field.

"It's got to be absolutely silent," I said, "when we go through that door there'll be fifty men asleep within a hundred feet of us. What's more, we'll have to be certain no-one is in the act of sending a message when we open the door. The three of us can't get inside all at once—that's impossible. The only door is two feet six wide. There are no windows—see the air-conditioning outlet on the roof."

"How do you suggest we get in then, Captain?"

It was desperate, but like all audacious measures, it could work.

"You two go in first, with your hands up. I'll come in afterwards with my hands up. They'll be expecting someone to be following us, and will look to the door to see why the hell he's bringing prisoners in there. They'll think we're three snoopers who've been taken by the camp guards. Okay. As soon as I say now, we all act together. Sergeant, you go first, and put yourself in a position to get any two of them. Simon, you take another one, and I'll go for the one nearest the door. But we all act together, understood, and you won't be able to look back at me."

We crawled across the grass to the outside of the pantechnicon, a step at a time. The grass was wet with dew and I was soaked by the time I got there. Once we arrived at the vehicle, I carried on until I was underneath it. I could hear the rumble of feet on the floor, and quickly identified the position of three of them. The fourth was difficult to place until he got up and walked to a desk placed almost behind the door. That one would be mine.

We could hear the clack of a sending key, and the voice of another operator. We waited until they had finished sending before moving to the edge of the pantechnicon steps, but then had to duck back suddenly when the despatch rider came from the tent, kicked his machine into life and drove from the camp. The sergeant climbed the steps of the pantechnicon and listened at the door. It was surprising to see how quickly and silently he could move. I saw the sergeant take his sliver of glass, and clench it securely in his hand. I took mine—this was no time for the Luger, or any stick-'em-up heroics—this was going to be in fast and act.

Simon took up his position behind the sergeant—I looked quickly around the encampment and saw no sign of life, and the sergeant nodded his head. No-one was transmitting. He and Simon put their hands in the air—I reached past them to turn the handle of the door to create the illusion of someone waiting outside, the door opened and we all walked in, our hands high. Two of them were together against the wall, headphones on their heads, listening. They showed no sign of hearing us enter. One was sitting to the right of them, in the depth of the caravan, at a telephone switchboard. He turned round, mystified, then looked past me at the open door as I had anticipated. The man at the radio behind the door, the one I had spotted from beneath the floor and marked as my own, turned round when we entered, and half leaned forward to try to peer round me.

I could see his lips start to frame an enquiry—I let the door swing partly closed to free my leg for sudden movement, and as his lips started to move, I called, "Now." He took the glass sliver in his throat and died instantly. The sergeant had grasped the two operators, banged their heads together, stabbed one in the jugular and throttled the other. The fourth man managed to rise half way standing—Simon chopped the side of his hand under the man's chin, his head snapped forward, his windpipe broken. He gave a horrible rattle as he pitched forward onto Simon's arm, already dead.

There was a fifth man in the vehicle—a maintenance engineer who had not gone off duty. He was lying on his back under one of the radio tables. Now he had a gun and was about to shoot me, right between the eyes from the look of the end of the barrel. The sergeant's foot came down on his hand, turned, and twisted up under his chin before he could utter a sound. There was a dull crack as the back of his head hit the pedestal of the table, but he too was dead.

I closed the door and locked it from the inside.

Simon, with his ever-present sense of delicacy, dragged the bodies of the five dead men and stacked them as best he could behind the telephone switchboard. I beckoned to the sergeant to sit at the switchboard—Simon held to his ears the two headsets that had fallen from the heads of the sergeant's victims, listening to both stations.

The sergeant found a card beside the switchboard listing the extensions. He gave me the thumbs-up sign. He was in business. I listened to the net of the long-distance radio. Someone was sending code in groups of five, and whoever was receiving it kept breaking in for corrections. I figured they would be on the air together for a long time. I couldn't tune the big radio to forty megacycles due to a heavy band of what sounded like local interference—I tried Rugby on twenty and got the standby signal. In those days Rugby used to transmit for one minute on the twenty, thirty, and forty megacycles wavebands, send a carrier wave for one minute and then go on listen for one minute. I picked up Rugby within a minute's transmission and tuned the receiver to the carrier wave. Now I had to tune the transmitter. Luckily the set had beat frequency oscillator tuning, with which I was familiar—you take a steady signal coming in, you send a signal out against it, and then tune your signal until you can hear nothing. Forty minus forty equals zero—it's as easy as that. My transmitter was netted to Rugby during the one minute of carrier wave, and the instant the carrier ended I called using the Morse key. At that moment a quiet bell rang on the switchboard. The sergeant looked around at me, waiting for orders—I waved my hand to him and he pushed a cord into a jack. The person at the other end spoke to him. After a while the sergeant began to smile, held the handset cupped to muffle his voice and said, "Yes, Lieutenant—I understand—everything is in order—and the time is zero one sixteen hours precisely."

I took the earphones off my head as he pulled out the jack. Rugby had heard me and would be trying Braintree.

"We're in luck tonight," the sergeant said. "That was the duty officer—is everything all right—he has a commanding officer's conference first thing in the morning and wants to read some papers before it—more likely he's in bed with a dirty book—so he won't come over, and what time shall we enter in the log?"

It took five minutes to raise Braintree, and by that time I was almost in hysterics. Finally they came on the air. "Sorry to keep you waiting, old man, but I'm not where I used to be." He was using the key at the other end and good at it—as fast as I was and I reckoned to send thirty.

My request for a plane was turned down flat! "There was a helluva stink about the last one—I didn't have authorisation and had to pass myself off as an Air Vice Marshal— what happened?"

"Brakes seized—bad maintenance your end!" I hadn't time for recrimination or gossip.

"Can you get back to me in an hour, and I'll see what I can do about a plane—though I can't make any promises. This isn't a taxi service, you know!" I knew—and I also knew we couldn't stay there an hour. I tapped the key steadily to interrupt him—I wasn't interested in his plaints about taxi services. We were in Europe—he and others like him had sent us there and now they could come and get us out. Or at least help to get us out. I sent my message precisely, rhythmically. "We can only stay here a maximum of ten minutes and I want a plane to drop the following, sulpha-nilamide powder and bandages. The location of any known minefields in the area of Ouddorp, safe passage across the North Sea on latitude fifty-two." I could hear him trying to break in, and let him.

He asked me to switch to R/T—to speak instead of using the Morse key. I refused—we had our own way of sending morse which no-one else could understand—we merely switched the dits for the dahs—it made rubbish of any message. A British voice on that frequency and every direction finder within miles would point at us.

He asked me to name myself. I did. He asked me what colour his hair was—but I had had enough fun and games. One night he'd walked in on me in a hotel room in Colchester without knocking. I was with a woman who turned out be be his fiancée—I hadn't known in the bar she had decided to break off the engagement the quick way. "Your hair is ginger," I sent back to him, "and some of the hair of your former fiancée is ginger, but her head hair was blonde four weeks ago. Now let's lift our thoughts above the navel." It had been his favourite expression as we had discussed his fiancée afterwards, man to man, and he magnanimously forgave me. Now he knew who I was we had no more interruptions. I told him to drop the stuff during the next night exactly two miles south and two miles east of Ouddorp. He was on the ball—must have had the map spread in front of him. I had a map on the wall—"That's in the middle of water," he said.

"I know that damn well, but we shall be in a small boat so I'll need the canister dropped from zero level. You'd better send for Cobhams."

I switched off the transmitter and waited. He came back on the air in four minutes—I acknowledged fast and he sent the message as if by Creed machine. "Couldn't land the plane, sorry old man, but too much going on in that area to call attention to it." He would drop two canisters, one with medical supplies, food and comforts (that meant a bar of chocolate each!), the other with the location of the minefields, weapons and things, and codes to flash at Harwich. The second canister would be fused to explode within ten minutes of landing—the War Office particularly refused to let him drop that stuff and leave it lying about for anyone to pick up—already Intelligence was having kittens about it. He assumed I would know how to defuse the booby trap! "It will drop exactly on four point zero zero, fifty-one point seven five from zero level at exactly midnight and check watches after this transmission. Good luck, good appetite, and hope to meet for another meal in Colchester, this time without complications!"

We checked watches, Roger, over and out, and off to bed, you bastard, in your pyjamas!

While I had been sending and receiving, the sergeant had operated the switchboard a couple of times without incident —mostly duty men ringing the cook house to ask about food. Simon, prowling about the pantechnicon, had collected four pistols and the mechanic's tool kit. There was a bag of stick grenades at the back of the radio console—he fused them and connected them to the mains lead as we left. Whoever switched on the light would blow the radios, and we hoped the pantechinicon, to smithereens. Most importantly, however, he found a locked first-aid box on the wall, lifted it down and the sergeant tucked it under his arm to carry it back to Jonfey.

CHAPTER THIRTEEN

The pig poultice worked, and pulled a hole in Jonfey's side large enough to take a golfball, which was just as well, since the first-aid chest, when finally we burst the lock, contained a bottle of schnapps, four glasses, and a pack of cards, all doubtless used during the long watches of the night when the ether would be silent, and duty officers abed.

People think of the war as a continuous burst of activity, but I never found it so. There were brief periods of intense activity when some action was underway, followed by long tedious periods of either inactivity or uneventful movement. Boredom, strangely enough, was one of the hardest things to fight, even on an assignment such as ours. Certainly we needed to keep alert all the time, but often for long stretches we walked, or crouched and ran, or crawled without sight of another human being and none of the false excitement therefore that comes from anticipated combat. Sitting quietly in this wood, watching Simon tend Jonfey's now clean wound, I was almost overwhelmed by a sense of peace and relaxation —I could have put my hands behind my head and my back against the bole of a tree, and sat for hours watching a float bobbing gently up and down on the tidal water. The sergeant, an oddly fastidious man about personal hygiene, had stripped off and was washing himself, splashing silently about in the water like a seal. Dammit, he was enjoying himself! He could have been in the water off Bergen, in those far off peaceful days, with a sun blazing down on his shoulders, and his only attackers the mosquitoes.

I wanted to get as close to Ouddorp as possible, as quickly as possible. When the sergeant had dried and dressed himself in the German's uniform, we stacked our few possessions into the motor boat, and clad as Germans poled the boat out into the estuary before starting the engine. We had lashed the Dutch longboat to the back of it; to ensure the farm was not connected with its theft, a last act of courtesy to the memory of the dead farmer, we towed it back inland on the running tide before releasing it. We turned round and motored up the south side of the water to the south turn for Ooltgensplaat. The channel narrowed suddenly just off the city, but such was our state of euphoria, no doubt induced by lack of incident and the motion of the boat, we steamed almost gaily through the heavy waterborne traffic, past the waterfront buildings and the small fishing port, a few lights of which we could see from sea level despite the intensive blackout. Most of the traffic appeared to be of cargo vessels, many of which I could see had guns mounted in their bows. Many carried timber, but most would be laden with food, grain, petrol and oils for the war effort.

Soon the Steenbergen polder was to our left, and in two hours without incident of any kind, we had reached the Zieriksee polder, land almost entirely reclaimed from the sea. Now the thin sheen of water over its surface showed where the Dutch had opened the dykes—only the high land round Haamstede was fit for occupation. Many hundreds of millions of gallons of water had flowed into this huge basin that had taken years to reclaim—the lives of the Dutch would be hard even when this wretched war was over. I knew a little of what they must be feeling. A hundred acres of our land had been under gorse for as long as my father remembered, and when I came of age and finished studying, I took it upon myself to get rid of that gorse. I ploughed it, bulldozed it, sprayed it with chemical, even hand weeded it when the young gorse shoots refused to die. But eventually, after four years, there was a field of rolling grass, rich in fescues and bents, my field. I cared for that hundred acres more than any other part of the home estate. What must it have been like for the local farmers, when they saw the acid salt water of the sea eating the heart out of their hard won land's fertility, washing out the nutrients on which their living depended?

"You're going to try the straight run home?" Jonfey asked. I was sitting in the wheelhouse, idly keeping us on course, about three hundred yards out from the dyke. He was squatting on the top of the wheelhouse to maintain the illusion the gun was manned, and that we were a German patrol. Simon and the sergeant sat, dozing and chatting desultorily in the bows—their eyes, however, alert for any eventuality.

"It's the best way, since they can't send a plane." There had been a lot of grumbling and a marked drop in morale, when I informed them of the decision not to let a plane land. I think Simon alone had the objectivity to realise there were other greater events taking place, and that even to rescue us, the 'high command' couldn't permit a plane to land. They had been little reassured by the news of the drop—the whole matter seemed unimportant as soon as we saw the improvement in Jonfey's condition—he was like a new man, the grey washed from his face, his cheeks flushed with colour. The swallow's egg was still tucked under his arm, but Simon was convinced that would go quite soon. How little we know of the human body—I can see that what hit Jonfey later was what we now call, with modern vagueness, a virus disease, doubtless introduced into his body from the pig's droppings. But I mustn't disturb the chronology of these events. As Jonfey sat on the roof of the wheelhouse I thought how good it was to see colour coming back into his cheeks, and how much more brightly his eyes were shining. Just after we came into the Zieriksee channel, the estuary widened—the North Sea was only fifteen miles ahead of us—Ouddorp about ten miles west north west. I turned the boat away from the south side of the channel—there would be no hope of sitting out the long day that was soon to come, stranded on the edge of the open polder, with little if any vegetation, and certainly no opportunity to hide a twenty-foot boat.

Then the engine coughed, spluttered and died.

It was like playing a game of snakes and ladders, and if you throw the wrong number, back you go to the bottom of the snake at the start of the board. All our future plans for escape depended on that engine, and I had nursed it carefully since we had stolen the boat, listening to its sweet running with immense satisfaction.

"It must be a fuel blockage," the sergeant said, but Simon disagreed—"It must be electrical to stop so quickly!"

I motioned Jonfey to stay where he was on the roof of the wheelhouse, and Simon and the sergeant to stay where they were. There were several ships about, and I didn't want to arouse any more suspicion than absolutely necessary. I took the cover off the engine mounting on the floor of the cabin. The engine itself was bolted to a board at the bottom of the small pit, not easy to get at. There was a direct drive shaft coupling it to the differential and the twin propellors. I disengaged the clutch and pressed the starter. The starter motor whirred, but there was no sign of firing. There appeared to be fuel in the carburettor, and the tank gauge indicated five gallons. I turned the motor again, with no result. I had reached the limits of my knowledge about engines. The sergeant seemed the most likely man to be practical about the beastly things—I called him aft and he came and bent down in the wheelhouse. There was a tool kit in the cupboard under the stair well—he spread it out before him and started using a screwdriver in a most professional manner. He took off the carburettor and turned the engine over. "See that," he said. "I can't see anything!" "That's what I mean, petrol should be spurting out of there! We've got a blocked fuel line."

A German Z-boat came sailing up to us, its vastly greater engines throbbing with her hundred horse power. It seemed to me her entire complement of twenty men was lining the rails. The duty officer came to the window of the wheelhouse and called through his loudhailer, "Is anything wrong?"

We took a chance and the sergeant called back—"Nein, danke, alles ist in Ordnung!"

"Who are you?"

I read the name from the wheelhouse log, and the sergeant shouted it. Someone on the Z-boat switched on a searchlight aft, and bathed us in light.

"Where are you headed?"

I picked the furthest point I could think of, at random. "Ouddorp!"

"You've got a long way to go!"

Damn it, did the man want conversation?

The sergeant shouted back—"Yes, that's why we are cleaning the carburettor."

"Do you want a tow?"

"Piss off!" I heard Jonfey say, with venomous intensity, not sufficiently loud, fortunately, for anyone else to hear.

"No, thank you."

"Where have you come from?"

Damn him, would he never go! I read the log—"Willemstad—317 Section, Inshore Marine Patrol," the sergeant shouted.

The water under his stern curdled as he pulled away with a shouted "good luck."

"Quick," I said, "paddle her into the side—the chances are he'll radio Willemstad to tell them we're having trouble —he sounds like that sort of interfering busybody—and they'll want to know what the hell we're doing up here. In five minutes, he'll be back!"

He must have delayed making his helpful call—but in ten minutes we were into the side and the boat tucked away under the platform of an abandoned landing stage. There was an old tarpaulin behind the stage—though in tatters we managed to drape sufficient of it from the stage itself to hide the boat. There were many trees nearby—we quickly tore off branches and draped them down, hiding the stage itself, the tarpaulin and the boat beneath it in a canopy of foliage.

Within twenty minutes the boat might as well have been buried.

Still no sign of the Z-boat.

I wanted to march them all away from the boat, from that vicinity which soon, I imagined, would erupt into a hive of bees, all looking for us with fatal stings, but the sergeant and Simon both demurred. Jonfey seemed somewhat comatose and didn't mind what we did. The sergeant and Simon wanted to get under the tarpaulin with one standing guard and one trying to repair the engine. Certainly without it we were lost, and daylight was not far away. Somewhat reluctantly I agreed. Jonfey and I withdrew from the water's edge up into the stand of trees, and I made a bivouac beneath an oak that would have defied detection even in broad daylight. Jonfey crawled into it. I imagined the biochemical reaction inside him when his suppurating wound had been drawn clean of pus must have drained his strength. Certainly his colour was heightened, and his eyes still sparkled, but he had no energy and seemed lost in a morose introspection from which I despaired of dragging him. He went almost immediately to sleep once he had got inside the bivouac—I had filled one of the schnapps bottles from the first-aid kit with water, and seeing his cracked lips contrived to pour a cupful of it into him before he fell unconscious. Then I left him and circled the wood to make certain we had not bivouaced in the middle of an active unit.

The nearest camp was about a mile away across the interminable dykes. There were fewer farmhouses about—the holdings out here seemed larger than back on the mainland. There were the ruins of a vast number of greenhouses—but whether the glass had been shattered by bombardment or deliberately removed to protect it, I couldn't tell. One or two of the farms were abandoned—I crawled through the barn of one of them and surprised two chickens—I managed to catch one, but the other started to squawk abominably and my nerves were already torn to shreds. In an upturned crate near the back wall of the barn I found a dozen eggs. It would be impossible to tell which had been there for a long time and which were still fresh. A pot mug hung on a nail behind the door—I brushed the dust from it then found a small galvanised feed-measuring scoop and one by one broke the eggs into it. Only four were bad, and these I threw away—the other eight I poured one by one into the mug, to take back with me. There's a world of goodness in a raw egg. I'd never tried eating raw chicken but perhaps I could devise a way to cook it. If only I had some of those smokeless pellets of metaldehyde I could make a fire, but with damp wood it was out of the question. One of the farm-houses yielded a paraffin lamp with paraffin still in it, and in another I found a large ball of gouda cheese. The outside edges had been nibbled and had gone green, but there would be sufficient in the centre for a meal. What with the eggs and the cheese and the paraffin lamp I returned to our bivouac like a happy housewife bringing home the bacon.

Jonfey's temperature had climbed too steeply too rapidly. His entire body was wet and he was delirious.

I half ran to the boat—Simon must have seen or heard me coming and was waiting on the bank. The lines of dawn were shooting over the land, climbing steeply into the sky in the spectacular display of variegated light. It would be a cold damp dawn—but we had no time to sit and examine it. I had other things on my mind than Disney dawns. I took him back to Jonfey, then went to guard the sergeant and the boat, our one lifeline home. I sat on the bank, half wrapped in the bushes. From time to time I could hear the clink of metal as the sergeant wielded his tools on the engine —he was having to tap the parts and though he was doing his best to muffle the sound it still rang to my sensitive ears like a carillon. The dawn soon became bored of shooting its coloured rays into an unobservant sky and settled to an over-all greyness. Mist rose from the water and coiled slowly up the bank, dank, cheerless, insidiously drenching, chilled and greasy as toad's sweat. After about two hours the sergeant poked his face through the tarpaulin and leaf screen. I whispered it was okay and he came up and out to stretch himself.

"Damned cold in there, Captain!"

"Damned cold up here, Sergeant! How are you getting on?"

"It was a blockage in the feed line. I got that cleared about an hour ago but stripped the damned nut when I was tight-ening it on again. I've been trying to work out a replacement."

"Will it be all right?"

"I should think so."

"Good man! Jonfey's bad. Simon's with him."

"Side gone rotten again?"

"No, seems like fever."

"That's unusual—the wound was healing nicely—I've never heard of fever once you get rid of the pus. How bad is it?"

"I don't know, but his temperature's very high."

"Is he sweating?"

"Yes."

"Good, that'll bring it down."

"I hope so."

"Where are they?"

"Along there in that wood—there's a bivvie under an oak tree, about twenty yards in."

"One of yours, Captain?"

"Yes."

"It'll be hard to find."

"There's only one oak tree."

The sergeant looked speculatively at the wood. "Would you mind, Captain, if I went? I mean, I wouldn't like anything to happen to Jonfey without seeing him, if you know what I mean."

"Yes, you cut along—there's some breakfast up there, raw eggs and cheese."

When he came back, I had coffee waiting for him. I got to thinking it must be a cold raw job for soldier/sailors manning those boats up and down the estuary, and it occurred to me that on a British boat, somewhere, somehow, the crew would have hidden from officers their own private arrangements for brewing up. I went aboard, skimming under the tarpaulin from the landing stage without getting my feet wet. It was in a rope locker forward—behind a coil of anchor rope—a paraffin stove, a kettle, a knife and quite a collection of goodies—coffee, canned milk, sugar, bread, liverwurst, ham, pumpernickel, butter—someone must have received a parcel from home, or raided a farmhouse store. There were even matches with which to light the paraffin pressure stove. It didn't make a trace of smoke. There was a can with more paraffin in it, and I made certain the stove was quite full. I intended to make a lot of coffee. The first kettle-full I took along to the wood. The sergeant and Simon were discussing Jonfey anxiously—it was plain to see how much both were worried. We poured a good cupful of the hot sweet liquid into him—Simon didn't know if it would do Jonfey any good, but it could do him no harm—the coffee bean in it was so adulterated there could be no danger of overstimulation— even to taste coffee in the brew was an act of faith.

All day long we took it in turns to sit by him and all day long the sergeant, or Simon, tinkered with the engine. Finally, Simon laboriously cut a metal and wood connector from a dead tree branch and a piece of the tin containing the liverwurst, and that finally stemmed the flow of petrol from the nut of the feed pipe from which the sergeant during the night had stripped the thread. He was full of remorse

—but I kept consoling him that it could have happened to anyone. It could, unfortunately, have happened only to the sergeant—a brute of a man, he had no idea of his own strength, and I can see him tightening that nut with the spanner in his enormous hands as if his life depended on screwing it the last eighth of an inch. Since the feed pipe nut was made of brass, the threads needed only finger pressure to make them secure. But I didn't tell the sergeant that. We'd had the same problem on tractors on the estate farm —so much so that I had forbidden our agricultural workers to attempt their own tractor maintenance, and wouldn't let them handle a spanner smaller than one inch.

I was waiting for early evening. We had a job to do, and then a midnight date with a plane and a canister that would not wait. There were less than four gallons in our tank and that wouldn't get us beyond the coastal foam. I intended to steal a barrel! I had worked it out. A lot of the vessels we saw on the river carried a spare barrel on the stern. There was bound to be a port at Ouddorp with a lot of vessels tied up. The engine worked perfectly the first time we tried it, and we headed into the stream, Jonfey lying forward in the gunwhales covered in our British uniforms, with the tarpaulin over him and only his face exposed, the sergeant sitting by him ready to cover him if anyone should prove nosy, Simon on the roof of the wheelhouse behind the gun, and me at the wheel. It was eight o'clock when we sailed into the outer port. The boom was up on the inner, naval port and quite a lot of shipping inside it. Outside the boom were anchored the fishing fleets, small cargo tramps, less important 'civilian' vessels. A police craft sailed round them as we turned into the bend into the outer harbour—he hardly glanced at us and continued on his rounds. Standing on the end of the line of anchorages was a fishing boat, the *Op Zekere Dag* of Rotterdam, the 'once upon a time'—what a world of dreams and aspirations must have gone into her naming—the young skipper buying his own first boat, dreams of rich independence. Certainly the war had played no part in his reverie. Lashed to the stern was a forty-gallon drum! The stern was facing out to sea. No-one was on board, not even a cook.

The police boat circled the moorings and went back inside the boom. The light had started to go and already our vision was restricted to a thousand yards of clear sight. We steamed past the *Op Zukere Dag* to the far side of the port with no desire to attract attention to ourselves, loitering with intent to commit a felony. I had always told my men in training—if in doubt, keep on the move, it's the still man, the loitering man, who draws your attention, of whom you ask, what is he going to do next? If he's moving, you already know the answer and never therefore bother to ask that or any other question. Our training had been practical—once, in a demonstration, I took them to walk through a store in Chester and never stopping stole something from each alternate counter. One of the lads tried it, paused to fumble something into a pocket and was caught by the store detective, a frightened little woman who was almost too scared to apprehend him. We cruised around the coast line until the limit of vision had reached five hundred yards, and then sailed innocently back across the outer harbour. When we got close to the *Op Zekere Dag* I put in the clutch and we floated gently towards her stern, our engine still running. Once we were out of sight of anyone ashore the sergeant scrambled abaft of her onto her stern, cut the ropes, and the three of us fumbled the barrel down onto the deck aft of the motor boat's wheelhouse. I let out the clutch, the sergeant jumped down, and we were away to the south-east with no-one the wiser—our inland route designed to still suspicion rather than arouse it. Once away from Ouddorp, we rolled the barrel carefully forward and stowed it in the bow. Simon used the mug in which we had taken the raw eggs to transfer the petrol, mugful after mugful, into our fuel tank. While we were transferring the fuel, the sergeant took over the wheel and we drifted slowly under the lee of the northern coast line. I went and sat beside Jonfey—his face was drenched, and the combined weight of the uniforms and the tarpaulin was serving to sweat it out of him. I've always heard you should fight temperature with heat—keep anyone as warm as you can who has a high temperature and this will encourage the natural defensive metabolism of the body to work. Any evil in Jonfey should be boiling from him. I turned back the tarpaulin and looked at his wound—it appeared to be very clean, and healing well. That didn't seem the cause of his trouble.

As soon as the tank was full I took the wheel and motored us out into the channel again.

Each of us looked at Ouddorp, Simon, the sergeant and me, and estimated the distance we were from it. It was hard to judge—since all we could see was a shadowy outline and a few subdued lights. I made the distance five thousand yards —Simon said four thousand five hundred, and the sergeant, pointing out that we were looking round the sides of a bay and therefore misled by the landfall, insisted it was only four thousand. The wheelhouse compass bearing to Ouddorp read exactly west north west. I spread a piece of paper on our small 'chart' table in the wheelhouse, and calculated the distance we would have to travel and the bearing to finish up just before midnight at four point zero, fifty-one point seven five. We arrived at what I judged to be the spot at five minutes to midnight, and switched off the engine. I've never known anywhere so eerie as the deck of that boat with the engine switched off in the middle of the Ouddorp channel. Boats sailed quietly past us, chug-chugging along their path into or out of port. Most turned seawards out of Ouddorp —only the smaller presumably Dutch-manned but German-guarded cargo boats turning left to sail inland. From Ouddorp itself came a constant throb of machinery, thumping out over the water. Occasionally, despite the precautions, we'd see the flash, quickly covered, of oxy-acetylene welding torches. The light had gone early, but now there was rolling cloud, the moon often obscured. The first we knew of the plane was the warning from on shore, and the anti-aircraft batteries south of us, presumably at Zieriksee and Haamstede, opened fire. We knew he would come in low all the way, keeping to the south of Zieriksee over the water at zero height, turn left in line with Middelharnis but out of reach of their guns, and then left again into the estuary, following the route we had come. He'd drop the canisters on his first pass, turn sharp left, over the Zieriksee polder where there were no guns, and run the gauntlet between there, Haamstede and Colijnsplaat, and out to sea-cocking a snoot at Domburg to the south and out of range. The most dangerous part of his run was off Ouddorp—he'd run across the front of the guns like a wind sock on target practice.

He came in flying magnificently, only ten feet from the water. I didn't see him at first, but then Simon pointed him out to me. The pilot must have seen us reflected in the moonlight—he banked slightly and passed what seemed vertically over us, lifting to about fifteen or twenty feet. I could see his face as he flashed past about nine feet to the right. Then the canisters dropped and he flicked on his landing lights for the merest fraction of a second, and was gone in a steep bank to the left. The guns started in earnest the minute he appeared, Ouddorp getting him dead to range. But their elevation was much too high—the shells exploded in the sky a couple of hundred feet above our heads raining spent fragments down upon us. The sergeant covered Jonfey's face and crouched in the prow. It was all over in less than ten seconds—the plane well out of the way over the Zieriksee polder, and silent the guns of Ouddorp.

I had taken off my clothes while we were riding at anchor, waiting for the plane—now, stark naked, I was in the water swimming to where I had seen the two canisters fall. One of them, time-fused, would explode out of the water in ten minutes from the moment of contact—our Intelligence was taking no chances! They were the size of ten-gallon drums, and buoyant. They had rope handles on the side—I flipped on to my back and, holding the rope handles in outstretched arms, back pedalled with my legs and headed for the boat like a maniac. There was no point in trying to de-activate the time-fuse in the water. The seconds and minutes hands on my waterproof watch showed three minutes and twenty seconds had elapsed when the sergeant pulled me over the side. We lifted the canister—it was surprisingly heavy—out of the water, and carried it down into the prow. The sergeant started the engine and we motored quickly across the estuary to the south side, away from Ouddorp. The timing device was of the knurled-knob type, with a fixed setting inside it —I had handled them many times and they presented no problems. My fingers were wet and slippery. I beckoned to Simon to unscrew it with his drier hands. We wanted no possibility of a drop when he took out that pencil-thin sliver of detonator which lay below the knurled-knob cover. He rapidly unscrewed the knob clockwise on its left-handed thread while I wiped my face and hands and hair on a towel we had found aboard. The elapsed time was four minutes and fifteen seconds. Don't hurry, take your time. The knob turned its complete thread. Now he would lift it off and throw it overboard. Then would come the tricky operation of lifting out the detonator. There was a silk or nylon tape to help—like the tape on a packet of cigarettes to help you lift the first one. The detonator would slide up and then out.

The knurled knob would not lift from the side of the canister. Damn them, they'd booby-trapped it, in case it fell into the wrong hands. Damn and blast them, where the hell did they think we'd find an electrician's screwdriver, the ones with an eighth of an inch blade, out here in the middle of the damned estuary. There's such a thing as being too smart. Simon raised his eyebrow, and looked at me.

"That tool kit the sergeant brought out of the signals HQ." My hands were dry—the sergeant heard us and threw the bag over to Simon.

"You bloody fool," I called out aloud. "That could have gone over the side." Nominally I was right, of course. Never

throw anything unless you mean it to stick into someone—
that had been a training maxim—but the sergeant and Simon
were so in tune, the throw perfect as the catch with not the
slightest risk. I was ashamed of my petty outburst. Simon
handed me the thin-bladed screwdriver and I inserted it
under the edge of the knurled knob. There should be a small
screw set into the shank on a spindle at the centre. If that
knob was pulled, the spindle would pull, and a nasty steel
pin point pierce the fuse and explode the demolition cartridge. Finis to us all. The light was bad. I couldn't find the
screw—five minutes and thirty seconds. The sweat, or it
could have been the waters of the estuary, ran down into
my eyes. Simon came behind me with my shirt—I could tell
it by my own warm sweet smell that can so soon go rancid
—and wiped my forehead. I reached up and used the shirt
to wipe my eyes. Simon stayed behind me ready to mop my
brow. Slowly I went round the side of the knob, feeling as
much as looking for the head of the tiny screw. Ah, there it
was. Turn it. For a flash of a second I forgot the principle
of unscrewing all these things clockwise. They are so arranged that if you tighten them anti-clockwise, they'll never
come off again—yet another of the nastinesses thought up
by the back-room boffins to make life in the field more difficult. I could feel the pressure of my hand about to tighten
the screw the wrong way but remembered and reversed the
direction. The screw turned slowly. It was a tight metal fit,
and screeched a little as it turned slowly round. One, two,
three, four turns. Now comes the tricky bit. Now you have
to feel that the head of the screw is in its channel. That's it.
Now gently push the screw down the channel to the bottom.
Now you can turn it again, clockwise of course, and it will
come out. The cutting of the screw thread is so arranged
there is a dead head. If you simply turn the screw clockwise,
without sliding it down that channel, it comes to a dead stop
and nothing you can do will move it. Short of exploding the
fuse, of course. Seven minutes and forty seconds. What's the
tolerance on these fuses—ten per cent? Five per cent? If
it's ten per cent it could explode, though set for ten, at nine
minutes. So in fact I only have one minute and twenty
seconds. Lift the screw out. That's it. Now the knurled knob
comes off, complete with the timing mechanism. That's it,
slide it carefully, that's good, and here it comes, tipping
slightly, finger nail under it and gently lift. Pass it back over
your shoulder, Simon takes it, and plop it goes into the water.
Eight minutes and forty seconds—twenty to spare! Wipe
your brow. No, Simon wipes it for you. I was sitting on my

haunches and had cramp in my leg. Now there was no hurry
—the timing mechanism had gone and the fuse was safe—
unless one of us was daft enough to hit it with a hammer.
Stretch your legs, take your time. The nylon ribbon was
fluttering at the lip of the canister—we were near the shore-
line catching some of the back breeze from the dykes. Not
enough to worry us, but enough to make the boat yaw a bit
from side to side. Now, get on with it, grasp the nylon cord
—no, wipe your hands again first—now grasp the nylon cord
and lift it gently, hold both sides and gently lift. The nylon
cord slipped from under the fuse and came away in my
hand, leaving the fuse in its socket in the explosive charge.
Oh winkle, winkle, I dare not use a pin, come out, come
out! Damn!

What did I say, snakes and ladders? Well, I had just
thrown a six and landed right on the snake's head, and we
were all sliding back down to his tail.

It would take a fuse extractor to get that fuse out—and
we just didn't have such a thing on board. They're made of
plastic, a plastic corkscrew that grips the inner edge of the
fragile aluminium tube in which is the picric acid fulminate
—or whatever other unstable substance they were using—
and draws it out, gentle as a baby's tooth.

Simon had seen this over my shoulder. I don't often give
way to despair—I hope that's not my style, but the look on
my face as I turned to him must have been one of sheer
misery. He bent over, I leaned to the side to make room for
him, and he examined the detonator. Then he whistled. He
took the nylon from my fingers. It had been severed, and
what should have been a saddle was two separate pieces
unconnected, with a cut between them.

"Somebody doesn't want us back in England," he said. I
knew, and he knew it was a joke—but when you came to
think of it, it was strange the brakes on that plane seizing
two hundred yards after he came in to land, and it was hard
to explain this cut nylon strap. Could it be someone didn't
want me home—couldn't stand the competition with his
fiancée? What an absurd idea! I laughed out loud—well,
not too loud, more a sort of a chuckle, which had the effect
of cleansing my mind and restoring good humour. I motioned to Simon to take one end of the canister and we
carried it to the side. I slid into the water and Simon lifted
the canister down to me. I swam away from the motor boat
with it and when far enough turned the canister upside down,
so that the detonator was on the underside, then rocked it
slowly backwards and forwards with my hand beneath the

detonator. After a couple of rolls it came loose and fell through the water—the second I felt it touch my hand, though there was now no danger, I gently closed my fingers and held it loosely, the water in my clenched fist acting as a padding to preserve it from shock. I swam back to the motor boat with the canister and the detonator and Simon hauled me aboard. We unlocked the cartridge containing the explosive charge, and laid it in the wheelhouse. The detonator we placed in the centre of the tin of coffee, where it would dry out.

In the canister was a knife for each of us, a tin of bait and fishing hooks, a gas pressure bottle and stove for cooking, water, a bottle of whisky, a large can of sulphanilamide powder and bandages, a compass, a sextant, and in a packet marked 'Top Secret, to be destroyed in the event of capture', a map of such minefields as the British Intelligence knew about. There were also three hooded flashlights, an Aldis signalling lamp which would work either from a torch battery or from a twelve-volt or six-volt supply. There was a black thin rubber one-piece suit for each of us, with elastic round the ankle and wrist and a hood which would grip tightly round the face leaving only the eyes and the nose exposed. There were also spring-loaded nose clips in case any of us felt like undersea swimming. There were two Webley .38 pistols, and a pistol I had never seen before with a stock for shoulder holding and a twelve-inch clip-on barrel. In the food canister was chocolate, with a packet slip saying 'Hello' from a girl at Cadbury's—salt tablets, tea, milk powder and sugar mixture, and a dozen tins of soup. The soup tins had an extra lid on them and complicated instructions. First puncture the tin, then prise off the first lid. On the underside of the lid was a black abrasive compound. Sticking up from the lid revealed below was a small black head like that of a safety match. Strike the match head with the underside of the lid. We did this, and the match head immediately began to smoulder. The can suddenly became intensely warm and I put it down on the deck. After a minute—the instructions on the lid read, you will be able to pour hot soup from the holes you have previously made. I grasped the tin through the protection of my shirt sleeve, and poured its contents into one of the nest of mugs the canister contained. Hot tomato soup ran out in a thick trickle. I can remember the odour and taste was absolutely delicious. Quickly, like children with new toys, we fired a can for Simon and the sergeant, and one for Jonfey. Simon stripped off the wound and dressed it with the sulphanilamide powder, just for form.

"It's not powder he needs," he said, "it's someone who can work out what's wrong with him. If he was an animal, I'd say he had a fever infection."

The word fever terrified me. "Smallpox, d'you mean?"

"I hate to say this," he said gravely, "and I wouldn't say it if I thought you were a person likely to panic—but the nearest thing I know to it is typhoid fever. Except that he has no spots. It's very puzzling."

I wished he had never said it.

"Is it fatal?"

"It could be, if we can't get treatment for him within another forty-eight hours. You've had all your injections, I suppose, sir?"

"Yes, of course, but so had Jonfey."

"He could have got something from contact with that pig muck!"

"But you said . . ." I could have bitten out my tongue— this was no time for recrimination.

"Medicine can never be an exact science. I don't know what's wrong with him, but I've had little training in human medicine. All I can say is he has a fever—and it is not the normal fever that can follow an infection. I don't think any-one of us will get it, but I can't say because I don't know what it is. There are a hundred diseases we know nothing about, even in animals."

"Is it your considered opinion—no, would you make an informed guess, that if we don't get him immediately into hospital he will die?" Ouddorp was not far away, and I would rather take Jonfey there than risk his life on the open sea, even if it meant prisoner camp for us both. Simon thought long and hard, then went down to look again at Jonfey. His face was now the colour of boiled beetroot, his brow covered still in perspiration. Where his system could continue to find all that water I wouldn't know. Simon opened Jonfey's mouth—his eyes flickered open at the same time and he tried to speak, but couldn't with Simon's finger depressing his tongue to examine his throat. When he let his mouth close, Jonfey smiled weakly. "Hope you've washed your hands!" he said, and slipped back into the dream world he had inhabited all day.

"I'm reassured by the fact that he continues to sweat," Simon said. "My advice would be to try for England."

The sergeant had heard our conversation. I looked up at him in the wheelhouse. He nodded agreement.

By now we had motored down the river and the promontory beyond—Ouddorp was on our right—I can never remember which is starboard and which port. The chart showed the possibility of a minefield about a half mile ahead. We slowed our speed and Simon was about to put on his black rubber suit when I stopped him. "You stay with Jonfey," I said, and put on mine. It was surprisingly comfortable, though the French chalk with which the inside had been powdered felt slimy to the touch. My sweat would soon alter that. Slowly we edged forward, Simon and I keeping a strict look-out over the prow of the boat. There was no other traffic here on the water, and once round the promontory we could see the open sea straight ahead. When we were at the point marked on the charts, I skipped over the prow and swam forward of the boat, taking it easy, taking my time. I had a rope fixed around my waist, a thin lanyard about forty feet long. Simon was holding the other end. When I came to the end of the rope, I paddled water while they slowly advanced the boat. Then I set forwards again for another forty feet. I was about thirty feet along the rope when I came to the first mine, floating in the water. It was a metal sphere about ten inches in diameter, with three detonators, like the butt ends of cigarettes sticking from its side. The mine was secured to a wire rope which went down into the water. I gave Simon the signal to stand still, and then swam down the wire. As I had imagined, there was a transverse wire about eight feet below surface level. Any big ship coming along would catch that wire, and pull the small mine onto its side. I gave three pulls to show I was going off the lanyard, and swam down and along the transverse wire until I came to the next vertical wire. There was about forty feet between mines. The lanyard was lashed to the vertical wire of the first mine—I untied it and guided the boat a good ten feet to the side of it, and saw them through, then went ahead again. The mines were all across the estuary, at distance of forty feet from each other on the transverse wires, and with about a hundred feet between wires. The mines were staggered in a crisscross pattern. Once I had worked it out, we changed course through twenty degrees, and sailed through the minefield without touching a single one on the way. Once again, the fault lay with the Teutonic mind and its love of orderliness—any British sailor would have taken a malicious delight in staggering those mines in a random pattern. The tide was running back into the estuary with a strong undertow. When we had taken the boat through the last mine I came aboard and sat on deck for a moment. Now the moon had cleared though it lacked its earlier intensity and we could neither see, nor, I hoped, be seen from the mainland. The mouth of the estuary was at least six miles wide further out, and I knew it could not be mined to the same pattern or for the smaller boats—any mines would have to be the big ones that need a larger pressure to set them off than we could give them with a small boat. When I told them what I had found we marked the positions of the mines carefully on the chart. However, the pattern I drew, through which we had sailed so neatly by following the twenty-two-degree lane, was now broken by one irregular pattern of mines.

"I pulled the wire rope five feet under the water, and tied a knot in it," I explained. That would move all the mines to the north five feet out of line! Any German boat trying to come through that minefield on a compass bearing, as we had, would catch it—right at the centre of the field.

We set our compass bearing due west, and opened the throttle. With plenty of fuel on board, I wasn't concerned about economy and wanted to be out of sight of the land when the dawn came. I had not taken off my rubber suit —the warmth of my body trapped inside it was comforting. We fed Jonfey with sips of tea and hot soup to give him the energy to withstand that enervating sweat. The sergeant lashed the wheel to a stanchion with a piece of cord, and came out and walked along the deck for a few minutes before going back in to take over again. I lay down on the deck with my head on a lifebelt and within minutes had gone to sleep. When I woke up, the sun of the middle of the day was on my cheeks—the sergeant was braced on the deck beside me, taking a bearing on the sun with the sextant. Jonfey of course was still unconscious, and Simon was at the wheel. There was absolutely no activity.

Seeing me awake, the sergeant smiled at me. All the tension of the previous days seemed to have drained from us, from me particularly during my sleep. The sergeant had washed, and from somewhere must have found a razor for he had shaved. His beret was tucked beneath his epaulette —seeing me awake, he took it out and put it on his head. I shook my head from side to side, sleepily, but he kept it there. He went back to the wheelhouse and soon brought me a canister of tea—I don't normally use sugar but we needed the energy and I swallowed it gratefully.

"Did you get any sleep, sergeant?"

"Yes, Captain. Simon and me, we split the watch and had four hours each."

I looked hastily at my wrist watch. It was two o'clock in the afternoon! I had slept for a solid nine hours. No wonder I felt refreshed, though I was hot and sticky inside that rubber suit. I stood up, stripped it off and motioned to Simon to slow down. When the boat was stationary I dived over the side. That morning the sea was bath and lavatory to me— I dived below the surface, as deep as I could go, until my lungs were bursting. The sea had been calm, and was as clear as the North Sea ever can be. I rose to the surface again, relieved, then swam lazily on my back, and on my front, taking large strokes to open my limbs. There was a sudden splash not far from me, and the sergeant was in the water beside me, trudging powerfully if not very stylish. His flesh was amazingly white against the water—I looked down, and mine too had the prison pallor that comes from sleeping in your clothes, from days and nights skulking under hedgerows, hiding in woods and barns. Dammit, we hadn't seen the sun since we arrived in Holland—not to speak to, anyway. I was completely revitalised when I climbed back on board. I sorted out the cleanest clothing I could find, and put it on. Then I went back to the wheelhouse, to relieve Simon.

"Good morning, Captain." I was surprised—he didn't usually use the rank. Suddenly I realised the swim must have restored in me the feeling and outward aspect of confidence and authority.

"Good morning—going in for a dip?"

"I think so."

"Peaceful night, was it?"

"We might have been in a canoe on Derwentwater."

"Know the Lakes, do you?"

"Like the back of my hand."

"I've been there a time or two."

"Climbing?"

"No, walking. How's Jonfey?"

"As well as can be expected. I wish they'd sent me a thermometer."

"Why—there's nothing you could have done with it except give yourself bad news! That's the medico in you, coming out. Why didn't you join the Medical Corps, by the way? They'd have jumped at you!"

"What, and spend my time patching men up so they could go out again and be shot at. That's not my style of medicine at all."

"You'd be saving life!"

"That's all in suspense as far as I'm concerned, for the

duration. You don't go to war to save people—you fight to kill. That's what I'm doing—killing, not saving!" It had been a thoughtful voyage for him, that was evident.

"What about the Hippocratic Oath?"

"A declaration of war is a suspension of humanity—an open confession we fail as human beings, revert to the animal kingdom and start again. Hippocratic Oaths, decency, humility, charity, chastity, generosity, oh, and all the other things I can't think of at this time of the morning—they all cease to count. After the war we'll take them up again, dust them off, and start where we were. Meanwhile we bathe in blood, stink of sweat and shit, and behave like rabid dogs."

Embarrassed—though I couldn't see why—he left the wheelhouse, stripped, and dived over the side. Within minutes, he was a long way from the boat, swimming hard. I would have tried to call him within a safe distance—but what was the point—why drag him back to an ethos that, if only for a minute or two, he sought to banish from his tortured mind. No man can kill in peace when he has cured with love—and though Simon ministered to inarticulate beasts of the field, he had love and compassion in an abundance. Killing had never meant anything to me—I hunted foxes, shot pheasants, grouse, partridges in England, buck lion and ibex in Africa. Granted I had never prior to the war killed human beings—but I don't think I had such a clear separation as had Simon between the beasts of the field and the beasts of our present era of civilisation—to me, and I know this will sound arrogant but it's the way I felt— the human race was a club, with certain quite specific rules for membership; I had no doubts about the death penalty for murder, and would in fact have liked to see it extended rather than curtailed. How unpopular that belief would make me in this era of permissiveness.

I think in his own way the sergeant felt as I did—he brawled and fought, drank and lusted, lived a life of the senses to the full—how could one draw a difference between him and an intelligent animal? I had Labradors at home looked at me in the same enquiring way, with the same intelligent 'May we?' expression, seeking permission to cock a leg.

When Simon returned we set off west again at full throttle. He dressed himself, settled down on the deck where I had previously lain, but I could see he couldn't get to sleep. After an hour I brewed a cup of the German coffee, taking care not to touch the detonator with the spoon, and took it to him. He smiled gratefully. "Sorry I sounded off a bit, earlier on," he said.

"Don't be!—what's the old French conundrum—je suis que je suis, mais je ne suis pas que je suis—in that case too, the man was following an ass!"

"Or the ass was following the man?"

"We'll never know, shall we? We'll have a drink together one day in a hotel overlooking Derwentwater when all this will seem a bad dream."

We could have gone into Harwich during that night, such good progress did we make over the placid water. The engine thumped away happy and regular. I stopped every four hours to let it cool down a bit, but it never gave us a moment's trouble. For most of the time, the boys were awake —since sleep seemed to elude them all save Jonfey. He alternated between unconsciousness, a mumbling fevered semiconsciousness, and for about ten minutes around four o'clock, a fevered lucidity. He insisted on being told where we were, what had happened, how we had got there, where we were going. The last place he remembered was the wood by the farmhouse—whatever had hit him struck quickly while we were knocking off the pantechnicon to communicate with Rugby. After ten minutes, he yawned, and fell back asleep. Simon was considerably cheered—"At least we know none of the brain functions has been impaired!"

Only then did he tell us men can recover from this kind of burning fever physically sound but with the brain of a child! I would rather throw Jonfey over the side than allow that to happen to him.

By our sextant reading and compass bearing, we estimated we were fifteen miles from Harwich.

I knew there were gun emplacements all along the stretch from Walton on the Naze to Clacton on Sea, from Landguard Point to Felixstowe Ferry on the north.

As first light came, we changed our destination and made for Clacton on Sea. We had seen no shipping during the night—though several times I heard the throb of big stuff passing over the horizon. Several formations of aircraft had flown high overhead, some from the east, some from England. We had seen an aerial dogfight, but no-one had taken the least interest in us. Just before dawn a fresh breeze came, and the boat started to pitch and roll simultaneously. We had to tie Jonfey down to stop him rolling about. He'd messed himself a couple of times, and Simon washed him clean with the tenderness of a first-year nurse. During the night he tried to be sick, but only a thin evil-smelling bile came from his mouth.

At first light the Polish Squadron came over. They must

have had that early morning randiness, the dawn urge that I'm told makes babies for unwary lovers. As soon as they saw us, they rolled over, dived down, and used us for gunnery practice.

It came as a terrible shock. We had sailed into the English coast confident our control would have warned all units of our presence—thinking we would sail in to a warm welcome. Instead of which we got a hot reception! The first fusillade raked our boat, and I counted five holes. There was absolutely nothing we could do except to zig-zag about in the water, but this was child's play to them. The second fusillade overshot us a little, but one hole appeared in the tarpaulin by Jonfey's legs, and the other came through the wheelhouse roof and shattered our compass.

There was no point in jumping overboard to try to swim through it—the hail of bullets in the water was as prolific as on the deck of the boat. I grabbed the Aldis lamp from the wheelhouse where it had been stored, pressed the switch and worked the shutter trigger, aiming the beamsight at the lead plane—BRITISH, I sent, over and over again BRITISH. It had no effect. I assumed the damned Pole couldn't speak English, until I looked into the lamp and saw the bulb had shattered. I threw the lamp overboard, and twirled the wheel, zig-zagging the boat like mad. The sergeant stood up in the prow and waved his hands vigorously above his head, pointing like some clockwork marionette gone mad to the English coast line and to us, trying desperately by sign language to indicate we were coming home. It would have needed a Jean Louis Barrault, or a Charlie Chaplin to get that message across in mime. Every time a plane slipped from the formation we could see the blast of those machine guns, hear the spit of them as they zipped through the air, mercifully past us. Flicks of water were chipped from the sea's surface; the sea beneath the stern boiled as the screws turned madly to try to get us away. The engine raced like a wild thing.

"Get down, Sergeant," I yelled. He was shouting up at the planes, "We're English, you stupid Polish bastards, we're English!" and then he took off his green beret and tried to show it to them. A fourth plane peeled from the formation and started its screaming dive, straight at us. I was looking forward through the wheelhouse window whose glass miraculously was still in one piece. Jonfey was stretched out in the bows, the sergeant dancing up and down on the deck waving his beret and pointing forward to England, home and Glory, and Simon, sensibly, was sitting to the side, crouched, making as small a target of himself as possible. "Over the side, everyone," I yelled, and Simon straightened out to jump—the sergeant took a pace to the edge of the gunwhale and I, a good Captain, determined to be last off, cut the engines. At that moment, the Pole's gun stuttered. It was a short burst—took the top clean off Simon's head, and he fell overboard into the water. The sergeant leaned over that side to try to drag him back in, but when he saw what was left above Simon's shoulders, he let the body fall back into the water and was violently sick.

One of the bullets had smashed Jonfey's knee—that's the end of his show jumping, irrationally I thought. The plane rejoined formation and headed towards Holland.

I started up the engine and went straight for Clacton. The law of averages had claimed its victim—one dead, one wounded, one ice-cold with anger, one half mad with delirious rage.

We were a mile off when the shore battery opened up— the first shot went about six feet over our heads, the second took us amidships. The boat folded like a jack-knife, and sank. It was surprisingly calm—I felt the boat sinking beneath me, and kicked myself free of the wheelhouse. Through the water I could see the tarpaulin-shrouded figure of Jonfey. I grabbed him and managed to get the uniforms and tarpaulin off him. When I broke surface I had him under the armpits. The sergeant's head was bobbing in the wreckage about eight feet away, and, happily, his body was still attached to it, though he was concussed. I kicked over to him, holding Jonfey under the armpits. A large section of the gunwhale was floating by the sergeant, who was just about to go under again. The lifebelt was attached to the gunwhale—I unwound the rope from the cleat and fumbled down one-handed beneath the water, gradually pulling the sergeant's feet towards the surface. Then I managed to push them through the ring of the lifebelt, and the weight of his boots pulled them down and through. His arms were floating wide, and the lifebelt caught beneath them. There was a welt down the side of his face, but the skin appeared not to be broken. He was breathing quite heavily, his breath jerking from him as if he had run a mile. I brought Jonfey's arms up, and thrust them through the lifebelt loops. It sank just below the surface, but was buoyant enough to take them both. Then I took stock of myself—I had clouted my knee against the edge of the wheelhouse, but that seemed to be the only actual damage sustained, except the ringing buzz which still continued in my ears. Slowly I trod water, pushing the lifebelt before me, making slowly for the coast. At that moment, I didn't give a damn if I never got there.

A motor boat was sent out from Clacton. It swirled to a dramatic stop beside me, and a Petty Officer leaned over the gunwhales, staring down at me in the water, and pointing his silly pistol at my head.

"Adolf Schickelgruber, I presume!" he said, his pink scrubbed face fresh with the morning scent of after-shave lotion, his teeth gleaming with Colgate's. God, how I loathed him and his wonderful war.

"No, you sodding fool, William the bloody Conqueror!"